Unlikely Saints of the Bible

Unlikely Saints
of the Bible

Surprising and Dramatic Character Sketches of
Familiar and Unfamiliar Personalities
in Scripture

by

WILLIAM C. FLETCHER

Illustrated by Dirk Gringhuis

ZONDERVAN PUBLISHING HOUSE
GRAND RAPIDS, MICHIGAN

To
Dorothy's daughter

Preface

It is difficult to write an introduction to a book such as this one. There can be no hiding the fact that these stories are not all cut from the same cloth. Some are written in the style of fiction, some in the style of an essay. Some have an obvious moral, some have no moral. But with all the variances from one story to the next, there are certain factors common to all of them.

Most basic, perhaps, is the fundamental assumption of all of them. This book assumes that the people mentioned in the Bible actually lived, and that the information given about them and their lives and their problems is sufficiently accurate for us to glean some understanding of them as real, actual, flesh and blood people.

These stories attempt to understand the Biblical characters they deal with in a manner that differs somewhat from the commonly accepted category for the people involved. This is not because there is necessarily anything incorrect with the traditional interpretations. But there is a need for every individual to re-examine the Bible, and there is little incentive to scrutinize any particular portion of the Scriptures if there is not more than one interpretation available.

None of the interpretations presented here purports to be the one true answer to explain the actions of the subject. Every attempt has been made to present the interpretation lucidly and compellingly, to make the character live again in the minds of present-day readers. But this is not to say that these interpretations should be understood as dogmatic assertions, designed to coerce acceptance of the particular point of view. A more correct evaluation might be that each of the stories is designed to entertain, and by entertain I do not mean merely to titillate the fancy. True entertainment should serve not only to pass an idle hour, but also to excite the imagination, to inspire the reader to further investigation and study. Indeed, if any of the stories of this book succeeds in challenging the reader to inspect again the Biblical data, to find for himself the interpretation that best accounts for the events recorded in the Bible, it is sufficient; the book has accomplished its purpose.

It should be emphasized that this book is not presented as a scholarly tome. I am not unaware that the book avoids many issues which are still the subject of heated controversy among scholars. This skirting of problems is not due to neglect. Every attempt has been made to confine the material of the stories to such things as are germane to understanding the issue of the story, and where a scholarly problem has presented itself, it has been consciously relegated to the background if it is not a point of fundamental importance to the particular story. This applies not only to textual and content problems, but also to the many unsolved problems of authorship and date of the various canonical books. I have assumed for the sake of convenience that the traditional views of authorship are correct; but I wish to emphasize that this is merely my own personal view. It is not presented as a scholarly issue, to be debated pro and con. Such debates would be far from the purposes of this particular book.

Since this is not a work of erudition, I have made no use of the apparati of scholarship, such as footnotes, indexes, or the like. I have included in the Appendix a short list of

Biblical texts from which material has been drawn for each story.

I must express my appreciation for all the help I have received in the course of this book's evolution. The list of those to whom I am indebted would be much too long for such a short work as this, but it would include numerous men of God who have served as my instructors, it would include friends of every description who have contributed a point here and an insight there, and most important, it would include my wife, who has endured my cogitations and loquacity as these ideas were developing, and has served most meritoriously as a critical reviewer with the patience of Job.

Contents

Preface

List of Illustrations

List of Illustrations

1
The Merchant

1

The Merchant

And He said, I will not destroy it for the sake of the ten.

ABRAHAM knew now Who this was. He had been aware of something strange from the moment he had first seen the men. Perhaps it was the way they walked, or the way they so suddenly appeared without his noticing their approach. At any rate, it had been more than mere customary hospitality that had prompted Abraham to spread before them the best that he had for them to eat. Now, though, when they had finished their meal, Abraham had no more doubts: This was God.

Abraham was not sophisticated by the standards of later cultures. He did not bother to ponder the imponderable. Forty or fifty generations in the future his children would wrestle with the ultimately unthinkable concept of the Almighty God becoming flesh and walking the earth as a man. But Abraham was not the sort to let his curiosity run away with him; so far as he was concerned, this was God, walking and talking to him as a man.

Not that Abraham was a mere child, a thoughtless primitive steeped in anthropomorphism, who would call anything he did not understand a god. Abraham had lived too long in the metropolis of Ur, he had spent too many years in the atmosphere of the highly developed religion of the East to be completely naive about divinity. He knew, as did the pagans of ancient Mesopotamia, that a god was not merely a more powerful man, and that the

15

statue or image was only a representation of a transcendent being of a vaster realm.

Nevertheless, the fact that the God of power was now standing before him as a man did not particularly concern him. He did not pretend to understand the miraculous possibilities of the nature of God, nor did he attempt to prescribe for Him that which He could and that which He could not do. If the Lord God decided to become man, if that suited His purposes, it was not for Abraham to question.

God was speaking to him, telling him of the immediate business at hand. Abraham was not unaware of the sin of Sodom, or of the wickedness that had already made that city a byword. Nor was Abraham appalled by the doom that God was pronouncing on that city. Abraham knew too well the lives that had been corrupted, the sorrows that had come to many innocents because of the unrestrained lawlessness of that city. Abraham felt toward the city as he would toward a common murderer, whose retribution was long since past due. The city deserved destruction.

But there was one matter which did cause Abraham some concern. His nephew Lot was living in that city. To be sure, Lot would never participate in sin with the other inhabitants, but if the city were destroyed, would that not mean that Lot also would share their fate? It was for this reason that Abraham remained silent and did not express an opinion when God was through revealing to him what He would do. He did not speak until the two companions of God — Abraham supposed they were angels — had left.

Abraham was a businessman, perhaps the most successful in the East. He knew the techniques of striking a hard bargain. So when he finally spoke to God, he did not talk of Lot at all. Instead, he opened by posing a seemingly academic question. "Wilt Thou wipe out the good too, with the bad?" Now certainly if there were a reasonable number of righteous people within Sodom, say fifty of them, it would hardly be just to destroy them along with the city.

Abraham stopped and craftily stole a glance at the Lord's face. This was the most crucial part of shrewd business. Depending upon how the other person reacted to the opening offer, the experienced trader could determine in advance how hard a bargain he could press for. Abraham certainly did not expect an uncontested acceptance of the opening gambit, so when God said no, that He would not destroy the city for the sake of fifty, Abraham nodded thoughtfully, but in the back of his mind he realized that this would be a good place to try for a hard bargain.

He did not dare to press his advantage to the limit, however, for this was no ordinary customer he was dealing with and this was no ordinary transaction he was making. This was God Himself, and he was bargaining for his nephew's life. So he was careful to show all due respect when he made his second attempt. However, he could not resist one technique he had found most persuasive in the past. Instead of asking for mercy on the grounds of there being forty-five righteous people present, he phrased it in the deceptive manner of calling attention to the fact that this was only five less than the other condition. "Wilt Thou for five destroy the entire city?"

Again the Lord acquiesced, and Abraham proceeded with fear and trembling — to forty, then thirty, then twenty. Each time God did not display any sales resistance whatsoever, and Abraham began to wonder more and more as the bargaining continued. This was much too easy.

Certainly there must be something amiss here for him to have so little trouble in paring down the bargain.

Abraham continued in spite of his misgivings. He had reduced the requirements for Sodom to be spared to a mere ten righteous men. He was about to proceed to five when a devastating thought occurred to him. He was bargaining with the Lord God, the Almighty! And God was not bargaining with him!

He could foresee where the bargain would end. He would reduce the terms to the absolute minimum of one righteous man, and God would not object. Ordinarily the prospects of such grand success would have elated Abraham, but now he began to be fearful. Suppose he did get the requirement reduced to one righteous man. And then suppose Lot were not righteous!

Abraham was fond of Lot, and no man is willing to concede that someone he loves is going to be found wanting when judgment strikes. But Abraham was just perspicacious enough to suspect that perhaps Lot was not righteous in all respects, even though he would not admit the possibility to himself. But if he succeeded in reducing the criterion to one man, then it would be proven one way or the other, incontestably and finally. The thought frightened Abraham; he was unwilling to take the risk of having his nephew whom he loved be put to such an ultimate test. Indeed, if Lot were unrighteous, Abraham would rather not have the bitter fact proven to him; he would rather be able to love Lot as a good man, even if he were wrong in so doing.

So Abraham left off bargaining; he did not press the transaction beyond ten. And when God saw that Abraham would go no further, He went on His way.

Abraham did not rest easy that night. Even after he had seen Sodom destroyed and heard that Lot had been spared, he would not rest easy. For he could never again trust himself in his love for Lot. He had been unwilling to be shown once and for all whether his love was justified in his nephew's life. Indeed, Abraham would be troubled for many years, from then on until the experience on Mount Moriah. Only when God had finally forced him to do the ultimate, to make an action in which there was no hope, would he learn how weak his faith had been.

For Abraham was not mistaken in his love for Lot, he was mistaken in his knowledge of God. Abraham had not realized the implications in all that God had done for him, in the promises which God had made and he, Abraham, had accepted. Abraham was quite right in thinking that he would be able to reduce the bargain to one without protest on the part of God. But he had not realized that he had stopped short of real insight into the love of God. Abraham not only could have reduced the requirements to one, he could have reduced them to nothing. He did not realize, and he would not until he had walked the road of hopeless, sacrificial dependence on faith for the life of his only son, that he could have simply thrown himself on God's mercy. He could have merely asked God openly to spare the one man he loved within that evil city.

And God would gladly spare Lot for Abraham's sake. For that is the way God acts with those He loves.

2
The Harlot

2

The Harlot

"I know that the Lord *has given you this country . . . ."*

THESE were not like her usual clientele. Rahab stood in silence before the two men, watching them as they swirled the warm wine in the heavy pewter mugs. They seemed almost too intent on the wine, as though they were consciously avoiding looking at her. Not at all like the men who usually came in here. A strange sensation, akin to embarrassment, came to Rahab and then was gone. She half-consciously gathered her robe to her; she pulled the folds of half-concealing, loosely woven linen closer about her, tightening the scarlet rope — the sign of her profession — in its intricate windings about her neck and waist and hips. The men did not seem to notice it; they drank slowly of the wine and swirled it again in the mugs.

Rahab knew better than to break the silence. Her income depended on knowing the inner likes and dislikes of men, and she knew when to be brazen, when to be kittenish, when to be quiet. Silently, her bare feet making only the softest whisper on the loose flax that served as her carpet, she took the fat wineskin and refilled their half-empty mugs. The men seemed to take no notice of it. Rahab wondered about these two, who they were, why they had come to her. From the moment they had entered her narrow room on Jericho's outer wall she had wondered. She had greeted them with her customary sign of hospitality and welcome, waiting by the door to wash their feet. But

23

these men, without saying a word, had motioned her aside, as though they were unwilling to remove their sandals, and that was most unusual. She had brought the embroidered pillows for them, and cups of wine, but still they had said not a word, hardly looked at her. Rahab was puzzled.

With a grace of movement that was partly natural to her, partly a learned skill, she returned the wineskin to the peg where it had been hanging. She turned and sat on the floor at their feet, her skirts spreading about her legs in a manner too perfect to be unpracticed. She lowered her head and looked at the floor, her long, shining hair falling in waves about her face. For several minutes they sat thus, the three of them, all seeming to be intent on a small area immediately in front of them, all watching every movement and breath at the edges of their vision. Then the older of the two men cleared his throat as if to speak, and Rahab raised her head so that for the first time their eyes met. With the first word he spoke, Rahab knew who he was. There was the unmistakable clipping of the words which she had often heard in the speech of travelers from Egypt. These men were spies, spies of the horde that had encamped beyond the river, spies of Israel!

"Is there no place in your city where the god Baal and Ashteroth his wife may be worshiped, wench?" Rahab knew that he was sparring with her, but for the moment she wished to keep her knowledge of their identity secret, so she answered the question as she had answered it on dozens of other occasions.

"Can the temple of Baal give you anything which I will not give you, my masters? More wenches they have, but do you imagine to find even one so beautiful as I?" She pushed her hair back from her temple with one hand, and indeed she was beautiful. She knew her beauty, knew that the fairness of her skin and grace of her form were more than a match for any of the empty, lined faces and gross, shameless bodies of the temple women. How many times, indeed, had the priests come out to her, smelling of garlic and temple incense, with their oil of anointing making greasy droplets at their hairlines. How often had she endured their cajolings, their promises of the blessings of their stone gods, their curses and thunderings when she refused their offers, for she well knew that their only interest in her was the increase in tithes they could expect if she should join the grimy ranks of the temple women.

The older man continued to look at her, showing no sign that he recognized or was moved by the perfection of the woman at his feet. The younger of the two did not look from his wine, but said, "Can you offer us the blessings of the Baal if we should come in unto you? Will our offerings buy fertile crops and fat cattle, will the goddess Ashteroth smile on our ventures as acts of homage to her?"

Rahab threw back her head so that her hair tumbled over her shoulders and on down her back. Her face was alive with a smile that on anyone with less grace would have been a sneer of derision. "Is my lord yet a boy, who still believes in fairy tales?"

The older man narrowed the lids of his eyes to mere slits, and said in growling tones obviously calculated to threaten, "The wench has not a cautious tongue. Could we not bring down the wrath of all Jericho upon such an impudent one?"

Rahab rose and went to the window, looking out on the fields in the gathering dusk. It was a calculated gesture, a familiar position, her back to the men, yet with her shoulders twisted slightly so that the arch of her back would be evident in spite of the loose, flowing robe. She laughed and said in a voice derisive yet warm, "Let not my lord play the fool. Does not the city know already the things I say? Why else am I driven here to this narrow hut on the very edge of the city? Who in this or any city plies my trade outside the haughty marble of the temple but those who have grown sick of the lies of a religion fit for children, not men? The elders know, my lord, even the king has heard, and the ears of the priests have burned with my taunts. Why should I fear such a dunce's religion, why should I worship powerless gods of stone and clay? Why should you, my lord?"

The older man twisted his beard, and said in a voice no longer threatening, "Tell me, maiden, why are you a harlot? Why have you not married?"

Rahab turned suddenly to face him. She was startled; it was the first time in many years that she had been called maiden, rather than wench or even worse. Her voice faltered somewhat, it lost some of the smoothness which was customary with her. "My lord, whom would I marry? Would I be wife of a man who snivels and trembles before a powerless god such as ours? Could I treat as lord and master one who dares not defy the fat priests of a false cult? Yet not a man in Jericho dares stand free of this lie. I did not marry, my lord, because I would not."

The younger man interrupted. "Yet why a harlot, woman?"

"What else is there for me, my lord?" Rahab's voice sounded more like that of a little girl than it had in years. "My family disowns me for fear of the people. Could I, with the other unmarried maidens of Jericho, join the ranks of the cult prostitutes, partaking in the lust-ridden worship of a god worth nothing? Nor could I glean the fields of the rich for a living, for landowners, too, cower before the Baal. Where could I go, what city in the whole land of Canaan would have me, disbelieving as I do? What else could I do besides harlotry?" She was silent for a moment, her brows knitted together. "And yet, my lord, mine is a sweet profession. I am a woman; I cannot fight back against this futile error. But when men come in to me, I can fight back. Mine is a silent battle, yet not without reward. For I, in this my profession, am an open affront to their decadent god. When men come to me, I alone with them can show them that this worship they feel they must perform on fear of their lives is a mockery. Is Baal a god? Why, then, can I, who defy him, give to these men all that Baal has ever given them, with warmth and affection besides? This, I suppose, is my real reason for harlotry, my lord. Through it I can strike back, I can show to the world my disgust with this child's religion."

The younger man had been looking intently at her while she spoke, and he leaned forward ever so slightly. "Is yours a winning battle, my sister?"

"Yes, my lord, I win my battles. Every man who comes in to me departs with the doubts my very profession has sown in his heart. How can he again be part of the orgies of the festivals without wondering at least a little, without thinking that perhaps these rites have less to do with Baal than with nature herself. And yet, I wonder at times. My people, the men of my city and the merchants I minister to, are hypocrites, all of them. Not a one has dared stand with me against this mockery which they really disbelieve — why else do they come to me — yet lack the manhood to cast aside. I have doubts about the success of my battle." She did not tell him of the other reason for her doubts, the vague, undifferentiated uneasiness which plagued her in the nights. She did not even understand it, and she could not. To Rahab, and to her generation, the only sexual sin conceivable as a sin was adultery; harlotry and promiscuous fornication were not known to be wrong. A thousand years of civilization would pass before mankind as a whole would recognize and know the torment that lay buried in license. But even though Rahab did not know the wrong in harlotry, she was not entirely at peace with herself. She could not be; her very nature as a woman would not allow it.

The older man seemed about to say something, but Rahab silenced him with a gesture. She listened to the sounds coming muffled from the street below. Suddenly she whispered, "Quick, my lords, up the ladder in the corner. Hide yourselves in the flax drying on the roof. They are coming for you."

Without a question the two men ran to the ladder, the older first. Just as the older disappeared through the skylight, the younger man turned to Rahab and said, "Why do you hide us? Why take the risk?"

"Because you called me 'my sister.' Quickly, hide! Your accent gives you away; by now all Jericho knows that Hebrew spies have come to my house."

There was a rustling of the flax as the two men concealed themselves. Rahab heard the younger man whisper to his companion, "Was I not right? Find a harlot outside a Canaanite temple, and you find an outcast who will side with us, who will rejoice that we come to destroy this idolatry." But then his voice was hidden in the tramp of heavy feet, the jangle of weapons, as four of Jericho's armed men climbed the rough stone stairs outside. Rahab quickly hid the two wine cups, then ran her hand through her hair and twisted her robe slightly so that she would look just the least bit disheveled, and her blood quickened with the excitement of the danger she knew she was in.

The men stormed into the room. "The king's order:

bring out the men who came to you into your house; because they have come to spy out the whole land."

Rahab's look of bewilderment changed to shocked surprise. Had the captain looked closely, he might have noticed that the expressions were too perfect to be genuine. "Yes, the men did come to me, but I did not know where they came from. However, at dusk, when the gate was to be closed, they went away. I do not know where the men went. Pursue them quickly, so you may catch up with them."

The other three completed their hurried search and returned to the doorway, their lack of success obvious, and the captain turned on his heel without a word. Rahab was careful not to breathe a sigh of relief until the three soldiers had followed him out and were down the stairs to the street. Then she climbed the first two rungs of the ladder and whispered to the men she had hidden, "There is yet danger. Remain still until I call you. Do not make a sound." She crossed the room to where the wineskin was and filled a pewter cup. She raised the cup and drank half of the wine, then refilled it. Then, cup in hand, she went over to the window and drew the curtains, leaving them open just enough so that she could see out. She did not have long to wait; soon, in the moonlight, she saw shadowy forms leaving the city, she heard the heavy clank as the gates were closed and barred, she heard the sounds of muffled orders and of hoofs galloping away in every direction.

For a long time she stood thus, listening, watching, sipping the tepid wine. It was not a very good wine, but to her, now, it tasted warm and encouraging. She wondered at the complete absence of fear or surprise which the two Israelites had displayed. Perhaps there was something to the rumored stories of wondrous victories, of miraculous food from the skies, of a mysterious, hitherto unknown God of power who provided for this people's every need.

Rahab wondered what it would be like to dwell in the nation of such a God. All her life she had looked for someone or something strong and real enough to command her respect. Her parents had told her to fear Baal, that he was the strength of Canaan. She snorted, and the wine in her cup danced. Baal might suffice for children and silly old women, but Rahab could as well worship the wineskin hanging on the wall. The women in the market place, the respectable wives and daughters of the community, who looked the other way when she came by, they were always prattling about the Ashteroth, the woman god, the universal mother who understood and knew women, to whom the women could come and find understanding and secret comfort; what fools they were. Could that stone statue, could those painted figurines understand even the pariah dog, let alone a woman? What could such a mockery of womanhood offer her, Rahab?

And yet Rahab knew that she was no better off than these silly women of Jericho. Perhaps she was not as well off. For all her pride and disgust with the empty forms of the religion of her people, she could not stand alone. Once in a great while, when she was by herself, when she could no longer quiet her thoughts by working or entertaining, she would feel a most unbearable sense of aloneness and emptiness. She could not stand by herself; life was too big, too frightening. She would ache, she would yearn for something — anything — big enough, powerful enough for her to stake her life on. She lived without religion; she sneered at the weaklings who followed lies in its name. Yet she could not live so; more than anything else she wanted a religion, a God she could believe. These times, the few and far between times, the times when her emptiness rushed up at her with overwhelming force — these were the times when the wine was a friend, when the wine could for a while at least fill the emptiness.

Rahab thought of the God of Israel — the Lord, wasn't that His name — and it was a delicious, exciting thought. Here was a God she could worship. Here was a God who had more to offer than lying promises of prosperity and lust-ridden sensuality. Even her occupation as a harlot had not removed from Rahab her loathing of lust for the sake of lust alone. Here was a God before whom kings trembled, who said and then did as He had said He would, a God who would not leave one deflated and alone when the novelty wore off. This God, the Lord of Israel, was not a chimera, was not a mere statue of marble or silver; this God was real.

Clouds were beginning to gather in the sky, making the moonlight patchy and dim. Soon there would be no moon at all. The city had been quiet for a half hour or more; the only sounds were an occasional growl as a pariah dog defended some choice bit of refuse, the shuffling of feet as the gate guards tried to fend off the first temptations of sleep, a far-off tinkling of sheep's bells outside the city, a whisper or two as lovers passed by in the shadows of her door — the normal rustlings of her city going to sleep. For a few moments more she listened intently lest she had missed some telltale sound in her reverie, but there were no noises which could mean danger.

She went to the roof and told the Israelites that the danger was past, and they could come out of hiding. She lighted a smoky taper, and its dim light made the room seem bright in contrast to the blackness of the night. As they entered, she motioned to the two to sit down on the cushions and she brought them two cups of wine. Then, standing at the window so that they could not see her face, she said slowly, "I know that the Lord has given you this country, that the fear of you has come upon us. No one is confident against you any longer, because the Lord your God is God in the heavens above and on the earth beneath. So now, please swear to me by the Lord that, as I have treated you kindly, you too will show kindness to my father's house, and save us from death." She turned suddenly to face them, her face a mask hiding the desperation she was feeling. If they should refuse, how could she face another year, let alone a lifetime, knowing that there was a real God in the world, a God of power, a God on whom she could base her empty and futile life, knowing this and yet being an outcast from Him, being unable to be of His people and be accepted by Him?

The two men were both staring intently at her. It was the younger of them who broke the brief silence. "If you do not expose our mission" — there was a slight smile as he spoke, for he knew that, should he choose otherwise, he could easily silence this defenseless woman — "we shall treat you kindly and faithfully when the Lord gives the land to us."

Rahab did not need to assure him of her silence; her face, which had come alive as he spoke, had told them more eloquently than any words could have that she now sided with them, that Jericho was no longer her city. "Up on the roof," she said to them, "there is rope lying on the drying flax which hid you from the soldiers. Get one of the lengths and bring it — it will reach to the ground — for the gates are shut and guarded. Go into the mountains, or your pursuers will apprehend you. Remain there for three days until your pursuers return; then you may go your way."

The older man was nearest the ladder, and he rose, handing Rahab his cup of wine. For a few minutes Rahab and the younger man were alone in the flickering light of the single dim taper as it filled the room with the heavy perfume of brush pine. A most extraordinary feeling came to Rahab: For the first time in her life, she was the one who was embarrassed, not the man. How often had she inwardly smiled when youths would stand before her, alone with her as she was now alone with this Israelite, and blush like girls. She felt the hot flush as her own face turned scarlet, and she understood how they felt. The Israelite was looking steadily at her, his eyes never wavering. Rahab nervously touched her lips to the cup which the older man had handed her; her fingers straightened a nonexistent wrinkle in her robe. She opened her mouth to speak and could find no words. She raised her eyes to meet his, but could not endure his gaze for more than an instant. His eyes had a look which she could not fathom. Her blush deepened, and when the older man climbed down the ladder, she turned almost too eagerly to take the rope and make one end fast at the window.

Then the younger man spoke. Rahab, fortified by the presence of his companion, raised her glance to his and they looked deep into each other's eyes. With one hand he took the tassel of the cord which was intricately wound in and out of her garment as a sign that she was a harlot. He said, "We may be released from this oath you made us swear unless, when we come into the land, you tie this piece of scarlet cord in the window by which you let us down and assemble your mother, father, brothers, and all your relatives at your house." He emphasized each word.

"With regard to anyone who is with you in the house, his blood is on our head if a hand is raised against him." He turned to leave, then added, "But if you expose this mission of ours, we shall be released from the oath which you have made us swear."

For a timeless moment he looked into her eyes with a gaze so intense that Rahab finally had to bow her head. "Let it be according to your terms," she breathed, and then he was gone. The older man was about to say something, thought better of it, and then he too was out the window and swallowed by the blackness of the night.

As Rahab drew the rope in from the window — it was much too dark for her to see the men once they had reached the ground — her thoughts were a disorder of wonder and excitement. She thought of the two men, of the younger one especially. He had driven a hard bargain. Rahab wondered if her family would be willing to give up their belief in Baal and humble themselves by coming under her infamous roof for protection. Even more, she wondered if she would find the courage to plead with them for their lives, to forget her years of bitterness and hurt, and call upon her almost forgotten love for them which had withered so much since childhood.

The signal she was to give was also a difficult requirement. He had stipulated that she hang from her window the scarlet cord which she wore (he had even taken hold of it with his hand). It was not a small cord, and because of its color and size it would be clearly visible to the attackers. But it would be no less visible to Jericho's defenders, should one of them but look down over the wall. Rahab knew that she could trust only in the God of the Hebrews to keep her from a traitor's death.

But the real weight of the signal lay in the other reason

the Israelite had for choosing it. The scarlet cord was itself the symbol of her profession; each of its loops and coils held some symbolic significance. Rahab could never practice harlotry without wearing the symbol; she was a child of her culture at least to the extent of knowing and inwardly respecting the rules it prescribed. For her to practice harlotry in secret, without wearing the open mark of the harlot, would be unthinkable, it would be hypocrisy, impossible. When the younger Israelite had demanded that she hang this particular cord from the window, he was actually demanding that she give up the profession entirely. His terms were that from then on she turn her back on harlotry and all that it carried with it, and trust only in his people and his God for her livelihood.

Rahab turned from the window and extinguished the taper, leaving the room black with the smell of the smoldering pitch. A delicious feeling of freedom filled her as she realized that no longer would she need to fight, no longer would harlotry be her sword and shield, for she had found what she had been fighting for. Here, at last, was a God for real men and women, a God with the power to move kings and shake nations. No longer would her intelligence be insulted by superstition, her needs frustrated by empty promises and idle threats. For now she knew, now (or at least, she told herself, very soon) she could worship a God who was so much more than worthy of her worship that she was actually unworthy of Him. She knew that the conditions for salvation were dangerous and difficult. But as she thought of this new freedom which comes from knowing the God who is reality itself, the conditions did not seem burdensome. None could have.

Rahab took off her robe, unwinding the scarlet cord for the last time, and lay down on the thin pallet behind the curtain. In the dark there was a smile on her face, for she was filled with happiness and contentment with what the future had in store for her. She knew that this night, for the first time in longer than she dared remember, her sleep would be sweet and satisfying; there would be no vague, ineffable feelings of remorse or hopelessness or loneliness; there would be no disturbing, impossible dreams; there would be no waking with a start to find salt tears in her eyes. For as she drifted off to sleep she was filled with a peace that she recognized was what she had been missing sorely for all these years.

Her last thoughts before sleep overtook her were of the younger of the two Israelites. She rehearsed in her mind all he had said, every feature of his countenance, the way his gaze had thrown her into such an inward turmoil. Somehow she knew that when Jericho had fallen, he would be the one who would come to get her.

3
The Nameless

3
The Nameless

Unto whom he said, Ho, such a one . . . .

THE times between Joshua and David were troubled times, and few there were in Israel who concerned themselves with righteousness. Doubtless there were some; no age is so corrupt that men of God are not found scattered here and there. But strange as it may seem, in those turbulent days there were even a few who were too much concerned with righteousness. Ancient Puritans, their misguided zeal drove them to guard their own personal righteousness even to the extent of severing themselves from the blessings in store for those who live humbly, compassionately, and according to God's will.

A few generations before the monarchy replaced the theocracy in Israel, there lived the unfortunate family of Elimelech and his two sons. Who is unfamiliar with the ill-fated flight to Moab, the sorrow of the short-lived marriages of his two sons, the glowing faithfulness of Ruth to Naomi, the warmth of the love story of Ruth and Boaz? As we read the short drama, captivated by the tenderness of their love, the chances are that we do not even notice a shadowy figure that lurks near the conclusion of the story. There, nameless, faceless, is a man who was so worried about preserving his righteous memory for posterity that he very nearly succeeded in having posterity ignore him entirely.

The summer was over, the harvest was in, the feast of

the harvest was held. Late that night, Ruth had come to Boaz, and, in tender symbol of her desire to be his betrothed, had lain down at his feet. Boaz, before the morning had unveiled them, had awakened and discovered her there. He was overwhelmed, not only by his love that had been growing throughout the summer, but even more by the undreamed of wonder that she was giving her love to him. Ignoring the younger, more exciting men she could have chosen — for Ruth was a beautiful woman — she loved him. But much as he wished to, he could not yet legally receive her as his betrothed.

Moses had given to Israel the law of Levirate marriage, a law of compassion whereby an Israelite was assured of descendants bearing his name even if death should strike him before his marriage had been blessed with children. In such cases, the unfortunate's nearest relative had the duty of taking his brother's wife and raising up children for the deceased, that his inheritance, his memory, (in a sense) his future might not be wiped out. Lest this duty become a burden, though, Moses had also given the provision whereby the nearest relative could waive the obligation in favor of a more distant relative. This law, of course, was standing in the way of Boaz and Ruth: Naomi, her mother-in-law, had a kinsman who was closer than Boaz, and he, according to law, had prior claim.

So, the next day, Boaz and this nameless kinsman conferred. Boaz, as any true Oriental would, came prepared to bargain. Rather than declare his hand right at the start, Boaz said that Naomi, Elimelech's widow, was selling (or, perhaps, had sold) a piece of land. Smelling a bargain, the kinsman exercised his right of prior claim, and said that he would redeem it. Then, almost as if he were commenting on the weather, Boaz casually referred to the fact that the transaction included a Levirate marriage to Ruth the Moabitess. The man flatly refused the deal.

Why did he refuse? A few suggestions have been made. Perhaps he was already married. The text does not say he was, but even if he had been, the social conventions of the day were such that the most jealous of wives could not have objected to a Levirate marriage. This was especially true in Ruth's case, for she had proved herself capable of supporting herself. Perhaps he was unwilling to expend a limited capital keeping up property for children who would not bear his name. But if this had been the case, he certainly would have refused such obligations from the start. As it was, however, he was perfectly happy to accept the burden of the property by itself — property which, by law, would remain in Elimelech's name, not his. These were not his reasons for wanting to back out. The reason he himself gave was that he did not dare take a chance of marring his inheritance. And if we were two or three millenniums closer to the time of the story, the answer would be obvious.

The kinsman refused because he was a righteous man! He was a man who was concerned with securing his own righteousness by scrupulously learning and following the law. As soon as he heard the word, "Moabitess," Moses' curse came before his eyes: "No Ammonite or *Moabite* shall enter the congregation of the Lord down to the tenth generation; because they did not meet you with bread and with water on your way from Egypt, and because they hired Balaam . . . to curse you." Small wonder, then, that the man refused. We can almost see him coming erect in awful dignity and righteousness when he heard the word, "Moab." God had specifically enjoined against intermarriage, and had more specifically pronounced a dreadful, eternal curse on all the future generations coming from Moab. The kinsman was a righteous man; would he then even consider being remembered as the father of a cursed family? Would not the better, nay, the only righteous way be for him to refuse to be so compromised? He would preserve his righteousness intact; his refusal was caused by his knowledge of God's law, and his determination to follow it.

But this was a blind knowledge, a blind determination. Righteousness without compassion is always blind. He was so concerned with his own sanctity that he failed to see Ruth as a woman unloved and homeless, he failed to see Naomi and the house of his brother Elimelech cut off without hope for a future. But more to the point, as usually happens, his soulless zeal for righteousness caused him to misunderstand completely the words of the Lord. The law had not cursed Moab without grounds; it made a special point of them, so that all could see that the curse was deserved. First, the curse was brought on by a lack of hospitality. But in the case of Elimelech, Moab had redeemed herself by giving him bread and water for ten long years of famine. Moab had opened her house to these destitutes of Israel on a scale far grander than she ever could have to Israel as a nation. Could this particular Moabitess be cursed for lack of hospitality? The second reason was Balaam's curse, the device by which Moab ensnared Israel through the false religion of Moabite women, who in marriage corrupted the true religion of their husbands. But Ruth had done just the opposite: ". . . and thy God, my God." Certainly Ruth could not be cursed on grounds of her having brought a pagan panoply into the nation; quite the contrary, she left the gods of her childhood behind, she placed herself completely at the hands of the God of Naomi.

But the kinsman was unable to see this. His was a conception of righteousness as a stern, almost vindictive force, without reason, without sense, to be followed at all costs. He failed to see that the Author of the law has the privilege of abridging the law, that He would never carry out this curse on Ruth, who had so explicitly shown herself innocent of the wrongs that brought on the curse.

This was a costly error. If he was unmarried (and he might well have been), he missed the inestimable privilege of taking as his wife a woman who was not only of striking beauty, but had proven herself without peer in faithfulness. Add to these the resourcefulness with which she, a widow, had supported both herself and Naomi throughout the summer, and the result is a woman who leaves little to be desired.

Even if he had remained blind to these qualities in Ruth (or if he already had a wife), he was completely unaware of the fact that Boaz was willing to pay almost any price to secure for himself the privilege of marrying Ruth. Boaz was in love with her, and when a man loves a woman, he does not care about financial bargains where she is concerned. And this is not entirely an assumption on our part. Boaz, remember, had introduced the subject by the remark that Naomi was selling a field. Where did this field come from? When Ruth and Naomi returned to Bethlehem, they were without income, and Ruth had to glean the fields of others to support them. There is no mention of a prior sale of land when Elimelech left for Moab which would now be redeemable. (And had he sold a field, it would only be redeemable on a year of jubilee. We have no evidence that the return occurred on a year of jubilee or even that Israel was honoring that code during those chaotic years of the judges.) On the other hand, Boaz is specifically mentioned as a man of property, so it would not seem too hazardous to suppose that he had started the bargaining by offering one of his own fields in order to conceal from the kinsman the fact that he was in love with Ruth — how else could he explain his concern for her redemption? And there is no telling how much property and wealth he would have been willing to give in order to secure Ruth for himself. Had the kinsman been less worried about himself, about his own rewards of righteousness, about his own posterity, he would not have missed out on these rich rewards which were in store for him, rewards of wealth and property without the slightest obligation on his part.

The tragic irony of the story, though, lies in the kinsman's overzealous concern with his place in history. Here his blind, egotistical zeal for righteousness caused him to miss out so completely that in any other circumstances it would be laughable. He was unwilling to raise children in another man's name. Yet Ruth was so respected of God that Obed, the son of her union with Boaz, was not considered a son of Elimelech's tribe, Ephraim. The law of the Levirate marriage was abridged completely, and he bore the name of his own father's tribe, Judah. And the nameless kinsman's blind, righteous worry about the curse of Moab could not have been more misplaced. Was Boaz known by future generations as the father of a family of outcasts? Was his name held in odium as being the harbinger of a cursed generation? What could be farther from the truth? Boaz' name lived on the lips of every Jewish schoolboy, for he was the great-grandfather of David the king. His name will live as long as the world survives and on into the countless ages of eternity, for out of his stock would someday come the Saviour of all mankind, the Son of God.

How futile, how frustrated, was the awful righteousness

of this kinsman, this Puritan who was so worried about leaving a name in the annals of history. The futility could not be more sharply illustrated than in Boaz' greeting, "Ho, such a one." So far from leaving a timeless memorial for posterity, his name did not even survive the few generations that elapsed between his death and the writing of the Book of Ruth. So fanatic was his zeal for a righteousness that had nothing to do with compassion, a righteousness that was important in his own eyes and nowhere else, that the writer of the book was more than content with inscribing this, the final insult of anonymity, "Ho, such a one."

4
The Patriot

4
The Patriot

". . . was not this what I said while I was still in my homeland?"

MOST of the prophets were patriotic men; Jonah, however, was too patriotic. His name appears in the annals of the kingdom as the prophet who foretold the expansion of Israel, and were it not for the short book about him, this would be all we would know of him. In a sense it is ironic that this man whose love for his country was all but unconquerable should be remembered not for his work in and for his own country, but for his work with the foreign, inimical power of Nineveh.

Nineveh rose to power during the eighth century before Christ. While Israel was declining into a state of lassitude and corruption, Nineveh was beginning to flex her muscles, making brief, savage forays upon her neighbors. As each year went by, tales of new ferocities trickled through the cities and countries; the world began to be apprehensive. Who could tell when this vigorous people would be welded into a united striking force and led out farther and farther in conquest? There was upheaval in the air. Old men sitting in the gates of the cities muttered about the rumors, there was a vague uneasiness that would someday — perhaps next year — develop into fear and panic. The lines of political demarcation were ripe for change; Egypt had long since lost her impregnable hold on the world, Jerusalem had faded from her brief time of power, and who would be able to stop Nineveh?

49

Such rumors should have bothered Jonah, patriotic as he was. And they would have, but for one thing. Jonah knew God. Had not God chosen Israel as His particular possession? Had not His promises all along been prosperity and blessing if His people would worship Him? True, there was a curse with the blessings; now Israel was foul with idolatry and unrighteousness, and she could conceivably be punished for it. But Nineveh was infamous for her idolatrous license, for her unrighteousness and atrocities. That such a nation as Nineveh could ever be allowed to tread the promised ground was so unthinkable as to be ludicrous. So Jonah had no fears about Nineveh. His was the task of preaching to his own country, to bring them to the repentance which would restore them to a place even Nineveh could never dream of holding.

Imagine Jonah's consternation, then, when he heard the voice of God telling him to go and preach to Nineveh. He did not want to go. Not that he was afraid of being persecuted or martyred in that corrupt city. No man who can ask to be thrown overboard far from land in the midst of a raging storm has any fear of what men can do to him. Nor was he a religious bigot who cared not a whit for the welfare of anyone who was not of his clique. No man who is ready to be sacrificed in order to save the handful of strangers who are the crew of a foreign ship can be called a bigot. He fled purely and simply because he loved his country, because of patriotism. Nobody knew better than Jonah the sins which beset his country. Suppose he were to leave his unfruitful ministry to his own people and go preach to Nineveh. Suppose Nineveh repented (and he had sense enough to realize that she very well might). If Nineveh repented, if she who had never known the truth were to turn from her abominations, what would be in store for her?

Would not God pour out on her the abundance of His blessings? Who could then stand before her, if God was with her? Certainly Israel, with its apostasies, its whoredoms, its deliberate spurning of the truth for a lie, could not stand before a people who had turned from ignorance to the truth which Israel was too proud to live by.

Jonah knew that if he preached to Nineveh, his preaching might be the downfall of his own country. How could he destroy his Israel, how could he be such a traitor to all the people and the places which he loved? And yet a choice had to be made: either he must destroy his nation, or he must refuse the command of his God. Jonah was a man of God, but even more he was a man of patriotism. He made the choice: he fled.

The decision was costly. Not that Jonah had any thought of removing himself from the pale of God's jurisdiction, as though his God were a mere local deity confined to the woods and rills of the Holy Land. Had Jonah subscribed to that silly conceit he would have had no fears of preaching to Nineveh (though it would have been somewhat of a waste of time). To the contrary, he knew that God was the ruler of the entire universe (indeed, he told the sailors that very thing). But he did believe that the proper place for him to worship God was in his country, where the sweet smell of the sacrifices could cover his sins. And he knew, too, that he must not be persuaded to go to Nineveh, for that would betray his country. So he fled from God's face. What a marvelous testimony to his patriotism! In order to avoid betraying his people, he was willing to cut himself off not only from his beloved country, but even from his God, for how could he worship God if he fled the place of the sacrifices? When he bought passage west to Tarshish, he knew full well that henceforth he would be a man without a God, a man without hope, without blessing. And yet he chose this, he chose to sacrifice his own happiness rather than to run the risk of sacrificing his nation.

Small wonder, then, that he could remain asleep when a vicious storm arose. Henceforth he was a hopeless man; what could the storm do to him? He had cut himself off from God; how could a mere threat to his life harm him more? In a sense, a man who is entirely without hope is also without fear. The sailors awoke him, asked him to pray to his God, but he did not pray, he could not pray, he had fled from the place in which he could have prayed. Yet he had compassion. The lot fell on him; he did not hesitate to admit his guilt, he did not hesitate to command them to cast him overboard. He did not know these sailors, yet he was unwilling that they should perish for his errors. Jonah was a man of rare stature indeed. Even the sailors recognized it: they ignored his advice, they risked their own lives trying to row the ship out of danger. When all had failed, they prayed earnestly for forgiveness of the deed. These were seafaring men, men who pitted their lives against the ocean, a rough, ready breed that knew no master but the captain, no home but the brine, no love but of hard drink and riotous pleasure. Yet even such men as these recognized in Jonah, a stranger and a Jew at that, a man of such stature that they were humbled. They were probably not very surprised when the storm ceased as soon as they had thrown Jonah over the side, for they had seen in Jonah the qualities of a man of God.

The raging waters closed over Jonah, and a miracle occurred. God had prepared a place for him. God saved him. But that miracle was overshadowed by another, a miracle that occurred within Jonah. Jonah learned that God will meet man whenever and wherever he calls on Him, that

He does not limit man to a particular time or place. Jonah learned that God's care for him was without boundaries, that when the terror of the crisis forced him to cry out in desperation, God was there, God forgave. A part of Jonah's error was corrected; he no longer put anything before God's command, not even patriotism. But Jonah still had much to learn; he still loved his country more than he loved God, even though he had learned obedience to God.

A second time God called him to Nineveh, and this time he went. And he was amazed. The rumors were right, this was a nation to be reckoned with. Three days' journey, an exceeding great city. Without God they were already a terror to their neighbors; what would they be with God on their side? The creeping fingers of fear for his country, the beginnings of despair for her safety were already growing in his heart. But Jonah had learned well the lesson of obedience. Stifling his fears, forgetting as best he could his love for his own country, he began to preach.

"Forty days more and Nineveh shall be overthrown." Never was there preaching with such conviction. Jonah was not really preaching, he was hoping, he was wishing, he was yearning that this prediction might come to pass. When he spoke there was no shadow of uncertainty in his message. He did not offer any rewards for repentance, he merely presented to them what was in store if they repented not. But these were a great people, a people destined to conquer the world. The message of Jonah went on before him, the nation repented. In the few relics of Nineveh which have survived there is mention of a brief period of national repentance; it could have been this very time. For seldom has the world seen so sweeping a conversion of a nation. From the king to the peasant the nation heeded Jonah's preaching. The people repented, and God forgave them.

What could be more disastrous to Jonah? His fears were now fact, what hope remained for Israel? With due cause he was angry. Was not this, after all, what he had said would happen? Was not this the reason he had made his abortive flight to Tarshish in the first place? Jonah was angry, ostensibly because God had used him to bring this disaster about, but really because he knew that henceforth his name would be Traitor. So little did he value what future remained for him that he was ready to be killed, right then and there. And then God spoke again to him. "Do you have good reason to be angry?"

The force of the question should have been obvious. Here was Jonah, witnessing a wondrous occurrence, seeing hundreds of thousands turn from their ignorance and misery and debauchery to the only true God, a sight which should have filled his soul to the bursting point. Jonah was a prophet; his was a life dedicated to spreading the good tidings of God, a life directed at showing people the error and futility of sin. And now Jonah was having the unique experience of seeing his efforts bear fruit, not in the lives of ten people or a hundred, but in thousands upon thousands. Few indeed were the prophets who ever saw such a glorious conversion because of their preaching. This should have been the very pinnacle of Jonah's ministry.

But Jonah was not thinking reasonably. Oppressed as he was with his almost obsessive patriotism, he was completely blind to the grandeur of the spectacle unfolding before him, and he missed entirely the gentle irony in God's question. Instead, with a desperate grasping at a straw, he interpreted God's question as perhaps holding some small ray of hope that Nineveh would indeed be destroyed. He knew better, of course. He knew that God was righteous and compassionate, that He would not destroy a people whose only sin had been ignorance. He even knew that the question was directed not against Nineveh but against his own blind rage. But a mind clouded with anger and beset with apprehension often does not think clearly. Jonah knew the futility of his desperate hope, yet he clung to it like a drowning man. With brute force alone he resisted the thought that was always trying to well up into his consciousness that maybe he, Jonah, was wrong, maybe his love for his country was a misdirected patriotism for a nation not worth saving.

So Jonah built a hut, and decided to sit it out. We do not know for how long he intended to sit there and await Nineveh's doom; perhaps forty days would have convinced him of his own stupidity, although it is not altogether unlikely that he would have remained there until doomsday. Jonah was nursing a grudge, he was acting on a thesis which he knew was altogether wrong, and it is not outside the realms of possibility that his mind would have warped more and more with each succeeding day until eventually he would sit there for the rest of his life, nursing a grudge the cause of which was long since forgotten.

Lest this happen, God spoke to him a second time. He raised up a vine to give Jonah shade, then killed it. Then He asked Jonah the same question, "Do you have good reason to be angry" — but this time He made the question specific — "about the gourd?" Jonah was angry about it, and with just cause: God had allowed a serviceable plant to grow up, then with no reason whatsoever had unmercifully killed it. What sort of compassion was this, which would capriciously destroy such a worth-while creation?

Perhaps even with these thoughts the light began to dawn

in Jonah's mind. But God took no chances; He went on to spell out in no uncertain terms the great omission in Jonah's thinking. He, a man who knew compassion, who knew obedience, who knew righteousness, had become so obsessed with the minor virtue of patriotism that he had allowed it to force all compassion, all obedience, all righteousness from his mind. Jonah had cared for his shipmates, he had even cared for a mere plant, but when compassion was in conflict with patriotism, not even a half million people merited his compassion. He had allowed his blind love for his country to turn him from a man of God into a ruthless, soulless monster. Jonah's error was not in being patriotic, for patriotism was then and still is among the virtues. Jonah's error was in allowing his patriotism to so narrow his sympathy that he had no pity on anyone, no matter how innocent, whom the winds of heredity and situation had placed in a position of political enmity toward his own country.

And the error ran even deeper. No one knew better than Jonah the stench of his people's vice and immorality. Yet Jonah, because he happened to be born an Israelite, because he was overpowered by the instinctive love for the familiar and hatred for the alien, had unwittingly set himself up as arbiter of the world's destiny. From the parapet of his own prejudice he was willing to sacrifice hundreds of thousands of innocents in order to save a people who, though his own countrymen, were so steeped in sin, were so deep in the mire of their own rebelliousness that they were scarcely fit to be slaves, let alone be a nation responsible for the welfare of the rest of the world. Whatever his claims, whatever his beliefs, whatever his knowledge of the truth, Jonah was in the last analysis not a man of God, but a man of Israel, a blind, heartless tyrant masquerading under the facade of righteousness and service and religion.

But Jonah was worth saving. His error, fully as much as Nineveh's, stemmed not from a willful rebelliousness but from ignorance, from a misguided zeal which placed one of the lesser virtues in a position too high for it to occupy. We are not told of Jonah's conversion. There is a small chance that he remained blind in his ignorance, that he stayed on that hill outside Nineveh, a wizened, twisted, prophet of evil for the rest of time. But God left no stone unturned; He was not willing to lose a man so rich as Jonah if he could be saved. Jonah probably left Nineveh a defeated man, a man humbled by revelations too great for him, a man without hope for his nation (and in twenty-five years, after all, his premonitions were realized in bloody fact). But in the last analysis he was a conqueror, a man who had learned that each of humanity's cherished hopes and ideals can remain pure and true only if surrendered to the unsearchable mystery of the will of God.

Patriotism is indeed among the virtues. But it has its time and place. Patriotism cannot be made the highest virtue, and there are even times, under the ineffable knowledge of God, when patriotism must be abandoned entirely. For God is the writer of history, not man, and even the noblest of nations must someday bow to the march of His will for all the peoples of the earth. God cannot be limited to any one people.

5
The Forerunner

5

The Forerunner

And all the people . . . acknowledged God as just,
when they accepted John's baptism.

JOHN the Baptist never had been a patient man, and now
he found it doubly hard to wait. The men ought to have
been back hours ago. When would they arrive? He paced
back and forth in his narrow cell, ever so often stopping
at the heavy door. By standing on tip-toe he could just
manage to peer out the tiny port through which they passed
his food. There was nothing unusual. The two guards were
still tossing dice at the foot of the stone stairs, and there
were no sounds except for the rustling of the prisoners
in the other cells and the monotonous moaning of the man
in the cell next to him. John scratched his beard, oblivious
(as usual) to how matted it was, and wondered again
whether the man were singing to himself or what. Obviously
the confinement had long since gotten him down: he must
be mad. Or maybe he had a devil.

John turned and sat down on the pile of damp straw
in the corner. The solitude did not bother him. He liked
being alone. He closed his eyes and pulled the short
skirts of the camel's hair robe over his knees. With the
smell of the straw and with his eyes closed, he could almost imagine that he was out in the fields again, watching
the sacrificial flocks of the Temple. A smile crossed his
face, a smile half of pity, half of contempt as he thought
of how many times people had called him a fool for choosing that means of service. "After all," they would say, "any

boy can tend the flocks; but you are a Nazarite, you are of priestly lineage. Indeed, were there not miracles and omens at your birth? Will you throw your life away?"

John leaned back against the rough stone wall and chuckled. They were the fools, not he. That was a good life, the best life. There he was free, alone with his God, his soul was his own. And few understood how much of a calling such a menial task really was. These sheep that he had cared for were the sheep of the Temple worship; it was a man's job. No mere boy could really watch over them and know each of the sheep by name, no child could really be sure that they were perfect and without blemish. Were not these the animals of the sacrifice, and was not the sacrifice the highest way of worship known to man? What was more important than insuring that only the very best would be presented to the great God?

John chewed idly on a piece of straw; he had positively enjoyed those days. And yet he had not felt completely at ease, for all along he had known that this was not his ultimate place in life. From his earliest memories he had known that God was preparing him for a specific task. How often in his impatience had he strained at the leash, unable to keep from asking over and over what that job would be. And then, on that normal day two seasons ago, a day just like any other, he had known that it was time.

A noise in the passage outside interrupted his reverie, and John was on his feet with a start. Perhaps they were back, perhaps the men had finally come with the answer John had to have. But it was only the guard, and John's face fell as he took the bowl from the guard's hand. There was a grimace under the shaggy, unkempt beard as he chided himself for not remembering the meal time. He went back to his pile of straw and started to eat. John enjoyed his meals, even here in the dungeon he enjoyed them. He picked out the fattest locust and dipped it in the honey, then popped it whole into his mouth. It made a crunching sound that warmed his heart. He was rather proud of his meals, he considered them something of an accomplishment. The first time Herod had come down into the dungeon to visit him, John had browbeat him mercilessly for his adulterous marriage, shouting out a tirade that he was sure would cost him his head then and there. But Herod was a coward, a pitifully weak little man. He had just sat there and nodded ashamedly, saying nothing, just as he had on every occasion since. When finally John had run down, having exhausted his vocabulary, Herod had recovered himself a bit and asked if John found things satisfactory. It was a ridiculous question, of course; what dungeon can be satisfactory? But when John had demanded his own special food, Herod had fairly jumped to give the orders. And well he might, John thought with a chuckle; what cheaper food was there? Who but the paupers would eat locusts?

John crunched the locusts and idly wondered what it was like to eat civilized food. Or wear the soft raiment of the cities. Or live in a house. When he had been out on the deserts with the Temple flocks he had not had the opportunity to try such luxuries, and since that day when he had without a word walked off and left the flocks, he had been too busy preparing the way. In a sense it was a relief to be in prison, to have nothing burning inside him, to be able to sit contentedly in a corner and think and dream. The last two years had been hard, frightfully hard. John did not like leadership. He did not like having disciples gather around him, he did not enjoy the task of deputizing men to go into the regions baptizing and preaching, he did not like having people look to him as the leader of the repentance movement. He had enjoyed the first weeks, when he had been caught up with the burning knowledge that Messiah was coming, that he must prepare His way. He had enjoyed preaching to the people, seeing lives steeped in sin change, seeing men come up out of the waters of baptism with a new determination, a new zeal for righteousness. He had been thrilled time and again as he heard reports of whole communities changed, men meeting together to study the Law, bands organized in a united effort to cleanse their ways and return to the code of righteousness. Yes, it had been enjoyable at first.

But then it had become more difficult. As the success of his preaching grew, so did his following, and soon he had crowds of people thronging around him as though he were a prophet. It had gotten so bad that even the Pharisees had sent men to him to ask who he claimed to be, for some of his disciples were spreading rumors that he was the Messiah. John picked up the last locust and bit down hard on it. Why had they misunderstood? Why had they kept wanting to make him something other than what he was? Why had they not been able to understand that he was nothing, but just preparing the way for the One who was to come? Some of his disciples had understood, of course, but the majority of them did not seem to, and certainly the Pharisees had not understood him.

He did not like the Pharisees, never had. On them John's preaching had had no effect. At first John had wondered why they even tolerated his preaching, why they did not have him arrested. But then, after a few months, he understood why. They were actually capitalizing on his preaching. The Pharisees had never enjoyed such popularity; as city after city experienced the sweeping revivals of his preaching, the Pharisees found it more and more possible to impose their ideas on the general public. For the first time in years the dietary laws were beginning to be followed, the Sabbath laws were being enforced, and the Pharisees all over Judea were becoming more and more the leaders of their communities. It was natural, of course; the people would look to someone to show them the way of righteousness now that they had repented and were seriously trying to live as God's people. But it had bothered John that they looked to the Pharisees. Not that the Pharisees were against the Law, quite the contrary. But the Pharisees had never recognized their own need for repentance; John more than suspected that a great many of them were really only hypocrites.

Well, no matter. The Pharisees were a tight, strong group, and even if they did tend to emphasize the letter of the law, John supposed that they could do as good a job as any of keeping the people on the right path. Furthermore, John was not primarily concerned with the leadership of the nation; his task was to prepare the way, to reach the people, so that when Messiah came, they would be ready to get behind Him and accept His righteous rule when He re-established the kingdom.

And that was precisely what bothered John. He knew who the Messiah was. He had recognized that Jesus of Nazareth was the Anointed One when he first saw Him; indeed, he had heard the voice of God call him "Son," just as God had called David His son. How wondrous then had been his task, how magnificent to preach the good news that Messiah was here.

But what had happened? John licked the honey from his fingers and started picking the bits of wing and shell from his teeth. This Jesus had done nothing toward reestablishing the kingdom. He did not even have a large following: a few occasional crowds, to be sure, but the number of those who were really loyal to Him was small. John had been preaching only a year or so longer than he, but already John's disciples had spread throughout Judea and beyond, gaining converts as far south as Egypt and as far north as Ephesus. John had been preaching righteousness — for who did not know that Messiah's kingdom would be built on righteousness — but Jesus had not shown much concern at all for the Law. Nothing seemed to be going right. Things had become so confusing that John had even begun having doubts as to whether he had imagined the whole thing, that maybe Jesus was not the one after all.

He arose and started pacing the floor again. Soon he would have that question answered, he thought. Where were those men? Two days ago he had sent them to Jesus to find out one way or the other, and they should be back by now. The impatience welled up in him again, and he paced to and fro like a caged lion, fuming and muttering to himself. He must be the Messiah. John had known that when he saw Him. He had felt it with the same certainty that he felt about his job of preparing the way. And yet He could not be. How many times had He broken the Sabbath? Five years ago that would have attracted little attention, but since the conversion that had resulted from John's preaching, the nation had turned back to the Law. So when the Pharisees had called Him on it, they had had the support of the people as they would not have had before John. Indeed, John's disciples had even reported that the Sanhedrin was considering ways to get rid of Jesus, to kill Him if necessary, because of His flippant attitude toward the Sabbath. This could not be the Messiah. But how else to explain the very spirit of God settling on Him in bodily form, like a dove? He must be the Messiah. But a dead Messiah? What with the popular fervor caused by his repentance movement, John did not doubt that the people would eventually support even putting Jesus to death, because after all, He did run roughshod over the Sabbaths and the dietary laws and all the other marks of righteousness. He could not be the Messiah.

John stopped and rushed to the door. He heard voices in the corridor. He heard one of his disciples arguing with the guard that by Herod's orders John's disciples were to be allowed to visit. John chuckled inwardly; another of his requests that Herod the chicken-hearted had allowed him. Finally the guard gave in, and, grumbling all the while, let the two disciples into the cell. John fairly sprang at them. "What news? What did He say?"

The two looked at each other for a moment, then one said, "He really didn't answer us. We asked Him if He was the one that should come, or whether we should look for another, and all He said was that we should tell you what we saw, the blind receiving their sight, the lame walking, the lepers cleansed, the deaf hearing, and the good news preached to the poor. He didn't say a thing about who He really was. But we did see the miracles. Do you think He's the Messiah?"

John did not have to answer their question. The passage from Isaiah rolled into his memory, and they could see from his face that so far as John was concerned, Jesus was the One. The guard was still muttering, so John told them to leave, lest there be trouble.

He went back to the straw and relaxed, his face wreathed in smiles. So he had been right, Jesus was the King. He should have had no further doubts when he had first heard of the miracles, but he had never thought to connect them with Isaiah's prophecies. And then the smiles left his face again, and a look of perplexity returned. If Jesus was the King, why was He wasting time? Every day the Pharisees grew more and more vehement against Him, and what with the popularity the Pharisees enjoyed since John's preaching, they echoed the sentiments of most of the people. How could Jesus hope to establish the kingdom if the people were not behind Him? Even David had not wrested the kingdom from Saul without popular support, and David did not have the Romans to contend with.

A mood of despair descended on him, for the more he thought on it, the more he could see that Jesus was heading for trouble. The miracles were fine for a few of the poor and needy, but the rest of the nation would certainly look on Him as a mere charlatan, not as their Messiah. Already the Pharisees were plotting to kill Him; there was more than just a bare chance that they would succeed. The people were looking for righteousness, not miracles. They would support a man who would lead the nation back to the righteousness of David, but they would not support a man who merely healed a few invalids.

And then a worse thought struck John. What had he done to prepare the way for Jesus? He had come preaching repentance, and the whole nation had caught his fire. But it was precisely because of this zeal that the Pharisees had gained so much ground in the past months. The people were striving for righteousness; they would follow anyone who claimed to lead them in its paths. John had prepared the way for the King of righteousness. But this Jesus, who was indeed that King, was earning the deeper and deeper hatred of the only group that stood for strict righteousness. Because of John's preaching, Jesus now stood with the threat of death hanging over Him.

And yet John had not doubted his calling from the first, all through the last two hectic years he had felt the presence of the very spirit of God. He had been God's chosen vessel, he was sure. How else had such a short ministry of a rough desert hermit such as himself resulted in conversions as far away as Egypt and Ephesus? John had been called to prepare the way of the Lord, he was sure of it. But the only way he had prepared for Jesus was the way that led to death. John was troubled. What had gone wrong? How could his labors, his own preaching that was by and through the spirit of God, have resulted in such trouble for the Messiah? If Jesus were to continue in the way which he, the Voice in the Wilderness, had prepared, that way would be the way of death. But this was the King, this was God's Anointed Servant, this was the One who would establish the Kingdom of God on earth. John could not understand it. He turned it over and over in his mind, and try as he might, he could not see how his ministry could result in anything but the death of God's Chosen One. John the Baptist was troubled to the depths of his soul; he was perplexed, he wondered about it.

And he was still wondering about it when they came to behead him.

6
The Thief

6
The Thief

"Jesus, remember me when you come into your kingdom!"

FOR a moment he did not know where he was. Then his memory returned, only to be snuffed out of his consciousness. Pain crashed in on him, a staggering onslaught so fierce that it forced his breath out of him in a cry. He gritted his teeth and squeezed his eyes so tight shut that tears trickled down his face, tears which had nothing at all to do with weeping. He willed with all his strength to faint again, to slide into unconsciousness even for a second more. The pain was unbearable; it was a monster, it filled the whole world, it shot streaks of lightning across his fast closed eyes. There had never been such pain; each instant it was a miracle that he could survive the pain, and each instant it got worse. The pain rolled over him in relentless waves, it was a bottomless sea, a gigantic surf crashing in again and again. For an endless minute he wavered on the very edge of consciousness reaching desperately for the blackness, aching to escape into darkness.

But he could not. The flicker of consciousness remained and grew stronger, putting a knife edge on the pain. He began to be aware of sharp points, he began to be able to identify certain nerves screaming more loudly than the background din. His hands seemed to be the center of the pain, and as he involuntarily tried to pull them to him their protest reached a crescendo that brought the edge of darkness in closer to the center of his half-open eyes. He forced

73

his muscles to relax, and the pain from his hands abated a little. It seemed as though his whole weight were hanging from his two hands, so he tried to relieve their burden by straightening his legs, and again he cried out against his will.

He opened his eyes fully and looked down at his body. He would have to use his wits to relieve the pain. He saw, then felt the block of wood between his thighs, and by clamping his legs tightly together he was able to take some of the weight off his hands and feet. That was better. He could breathe a little easier now, the pain had receded to an almost bearable level. He wondered how long he had been unconscious. Letting his head fall to the right he could see the other cross standing where it had been raised a minute or so before they had raised his upright. Then they had dropped it into the hole with an impossible lurch which had been the last thing he remembered. He could not have been unconscious for very long, for they had just finished driving the nails into the third man, and were in the process of raising His cross as the center of the three.

As he watched, the four soldiers raised the third cross and dropped it the three feet or so into the hole that awaited it. It hit the bottom with a jar that almost tore the hands and feet off. He watched aghast — he knew how it felt — but this man did not utter even a gasp. Feeling for an instant the unbearable memory of that moment, he closed his eyes, and, painful as were his own hands and feet, he was able to breathe a little easier as he realized that for a few sweet moments at least the third man could enjoy the comfort of unconsciousness. He opened his eyes and looked again, and his stomach coiled into a knot. The third man was not unconscious: His eyes were open in a stare that was a little bit glassy, the muscles of His jaws stood out from His face as tooth strained against tooth, but He had not even cried out. Unable to bear the sight, he shut his eyes, the memory of his own brief instant of that torture rushed again at him, his imagination staggered at the thought of the pain this man must be bearing, unable to pass into oblivion, and his stomach lurched as his mind writhed at the thought. He leaned his head forward and vomited, and the blackness closed in on him again.

Too soon, too soon, he thought, as the darkness began to fade again. Like a child trying to escape the burden of awakening in the morning he tried to pull the covers of unconsciousness over his head, but he could not keep back the dawn. Like a span of ravenous lions released by their master the pain rushed at him, and he instantly clamped his thighs together to support his body. He felt vaguely superior as the pain faded a bit, as though he had outsmarted the lions. The man on the far cross was awake now, awake and screaming at the top of his lungs. With an idiot's smile he considered the action, and it seemed like a worthy thing to do. He opened his mouth wide and he too screamed, screamed as loud as he could, screamed and screamed and screamed, pausing only to draw in breath for the next scream. The other's voice was blotted out, his own pain was curtained by his screaming, his mind began to relax and he felt quite proud of himself for discovering this glorious way to conquer the pain. He would scream it right out of existence. For three or four full minutes he screamed with all his strength.

With a snap his mind returned to reality, and he clamped his teeth down hard on his tongue to cut off his screams. This was madness, this was lunacy, this was surrendering to the pain, and he knew that if he did surrender his mind would sink forever into the bottomless abyss of horror that was insanity. With an effort of will he forced his mind off himself, off his pain. He looked at his shadow, and saw that it was but a little past noon. He took some comfort in the thought that in six hours he would be dead. At least his suffering would not be spread over three or four days. He breathed a prayer of thanks to God that tomorrow was the Passover and they would not allow him to remain on the cross past sundown today.

And yet it was a bleak sort of comfort. He knew full well what to expect at death, he had rehearsed it over and over in his mind during the past few hours. He knew that he would go to Sheol as everyone did, and it was not a very appealing place. He remembered that only a few days ago he had been talking with a Greek merchant, and how impressed he had been when the Greek had described — what was his name for it — *hades*. The Greek had told him of it, of the emptiness, the hopelessness, of the shadowy half existence, of the chill lack of passion and feeling, of the complete absence of justice and injustice. The Greek's description had tallied point for point with what he knew of Sheol. Evidently God had revealed to everyone on earth what awaited after death, and, although it was not a place to which anyone in his right mind would want to go, at least there would be no more of this impossible pain. Confronted by the pain, he had little trouble reconciling himself to death, although in the shadows of his mind there still lurked the creeping fingers of dread which all men feel when they think on death. But these nameless, formless horrors could not bother him now; the pain was much too great.

It was really amazing that it could be so intense. He remembered the time when he was a child and a ram had butted him in the stomach, knocking his breath out, and for an instant the pain had seemed the very acme of torture. But this pain, this cross convinced him how wrong he had been. It was strange; it was almost as though a demon were playing on a great harp of torture. His hands and feet were no longer so unbearable, he had become a little bit accustomed to them, so that they had been relegated into the near background, a thunderous swell on which the other pain danced. There was much pain from his mouth; evidently he had chipped one of his front teeth when the cross had dropped into position, for every time he inhaled through his mouth a firebrand seared into his thoughts. His tongue was smarting with a throbbing rhythm where he had bitten it, and there was the unpleasant taste of blood. His stomach was still queasy, and the smell of vomit served to keep it on edge. His head ached now and again, unprotected as it was against the hot sun, and there was the annoying trickle of sweat as a drop ran now down the bridge of his nose, now down his ribs, now down the calf of his leg. He looked over to the man on the center cross, and he knew how much more uncomfortable He must be as the sweat mingled with the blood from His forehead and trickled down His face. There was a spot of blood at the corner of that man's mouth, and he knew that He, too, had gnawed His tongue because of the pain.

There was a buzzing sound at his right ear, and he turned his head quickly to see what it was. The shocks of pain caused by the sudden movement made him gasp and grit his teeth. He need not have turned, for the source of the buzzing soon became evident and the horse-fly landed on his nose. He crossed his eyes in a ludicrous attempt to inspect the fly, and he was furious at its audacity, its insult. He raised his lower lip and blew the fly off his nose. It buzzed around for a second or two, then chose a new landing place, his left cheek. It tickled. He opened and closed his mouth and grimaced in a futile attempt to dislodge the intruder. He strained his eyes downward, but it was just outside his field of vision. He clenched his teeth and tried to endure, hoping his patience could outlast the fly's. Then the horse-fly bit. He involuntarily tried to slap it with his left hand, and the bolt of pain brought the darkness in at the edges of his vision, made the white spots dance before him. The fly bit again, then a third time.

It was too much. His helplessness before this insignificant fly loomed before him, and he broke down and wept unashamedly, like a child. Tears coursed down his face, and mountains of despair welled up in him. Was not this the way it had been all his life? Here he was bearing up with all his courage on the cross, the cruelest torment man could devise, nailed hand and foot, racked with pain, yet bearing it like a man, and then this fly, this ridiculous, tiny insult that a little girl could crush, this mere horse-fly was his master. He thought of his life, and it seemed cut from this very pattern. He had not made excessive demands from life; he had not cursed his humble birth nor envied the fortunate, he had not asked kingdoms or wealth or ease, he had not mourned for days filled with bliss. He had all his life believed in God, he had always done his very best to obey the Law, he had tried to live peaceably and dutifully. He had not asked for a beautiful wife, but had been more than content with the girl he had loved — what was her name? Absurd! She had been his betrothed for over two years, he had loved her as himself, yet now, on this hot cross, he could not remember even her name. What was it?

And yet, in spite of the fact that he had worked his

hardest at the jobs he had had, in spite of his scrimping and hoarding to live on what he made, he had been unable to. Where was justice, where was righteousness, what justification was there in life, when he and so many like him had to filch and steal in order to eke out a bare survival. God must be a tyrant — blasphemy! — a cruel master who took delight in seeing the poor, the humble starve in a society ruled by the rich with no regard to those born under the curse of poverty. A torrent of bitterness filled his soul; he was almost glad to be dying, to be leaving a world in which justice was a myth unless you were born rich or fortunate. This death, this death on the cross of the condemned, was it not a fitting climax to the bad joke of life? He thought of his Great Crime, and now he did not care particularly that it had not succeeded. Not that it was the first time he had been forced by the exigencies of hunger and want to break the law. It was not the first time and it was not the thirty-first time. But this time he had made the mistake of trying to rob a Roman at knife point, trying to get enough coins to buy stale bread to fill his stomach. He had been caught in the act. How long ago was that? It seemed at least a year, maybe two, but in reality it was only yesterday evening.

Then the fly was gone, and he breathed a sigh of relief. For the first time he noticed the crowd gathered round. He was surprised at its number; there must have been over a hundred of the curious and the mourners. He pitied them, even though he was the one to be pitied. But he was leaving. He was dying, going to a world which if no better than this, at least was not ruled by kings and petty economic tyrants who made a mockery of justice. He pitied the people he saw, he felt almost happy that he would no longer be faced with the daily task of trying to live righteously, trying to live a life at peace with himself, yet find-ing his way blocked at every turn by barriers too great to be hurdled.

Again he had to force his mind back to reality. What right had he to be so self-piteous? He looked again at the middle cross. There, there was a man to be pitied. The guard who had walked beside him this morning as he carried the weight of his own cross had talked of Him, had even sounded as though he were against this particular cruci-fixion (a Roman? Preposterous). He had told a fellow soldier of Pilate's attempt to free this Jesus, he had sneered at the way the Jews had stirred up the mob to violence in order to vent their spleen on this uncondemned man. He had even told (albeit with a slight sneer) of the rumor that this man claimed to be a god. Much as he felt his own case to be unfair, his anger rose a bit as he looked over to the man on the cross next to him. What bitterness He should feel, and yet He did not act at all vindictive. The look on His face was one of sorrow and pity rather than bitterness and pain. He marveled that he had not heard the man utter a cry. Perhaps there was something out of the ordinary about the man, for he knew the pain, and he knew that it was impossible not to cry out underneath it.

The pain had a different complexion now. His hands and feet were beginning to throb mercilessly as the blood began to clot. His whole back felt raw from the chafing and the splinters. And worst of all was the torture of having to keep his thighs clamped together. His muscles ached all the way from his knees to the middle of his stom-ach, unaccustomed as they were to the task of squeezing his legs together hard enough to support his weight. He longed to relax them, the thought was a real temptation, but he knew from bitter experience the agony that would

come from even a moment's release. He looked again at
the man to his right, and he knew that by now the cuts
around His head and the bruises and welts on His face
must be torturing Him mercilessly. He was thankful that
he had not had to endure the ignominy that this man had
suffered, for he recognized that such welts could be caused
by nothing other than hands and fists. He noticed for the
first time that there was a sign on that cross, and, although
he could not read, he had seen the words *Rex* and *Judae-*
orum often enough to get an idea of the sarcasm and insult
implied.

The crowd was beginning to move around a bit. Evidently the lust of the bloodthirsty had begun to be appeased,
and they were growing restive. They seemed to congregate
around the center cross, as though He were their special
victim. Several times one of the crowd would laugh in
the face of the man who was suffering there, fingers would
point and heads would wag. A shout rose above the growing tumult, "He saved others; let him save himself, if he
is the Christ of God, his Chosen One." There was a general
roar of laughter and approval, and another voice picked up
the theme, "Aha! You who would destroy the temple and
build it in three days, save yourself, and come down from
the cross!"

He wondered at that last shout. Although he had never
seen the man before, he respected the man on the central
cross, respected Him a great deal for the way He was en-
during the torture. This was not the sort of man to make
fantastic claims. Had He really made such a statement?
If the man had really said it, he was almost willing to believe that He could do it. He was certainly proving that
He was a man of exceptional power to withstand such pain
without making a sound.

A man closer to Him, dressed in the rich robes of the Sanhedrin, shouted out, "He saved others; himself he cannot save. The Christ, the King of Israel! Let him now come down from the cross, so that we may see and believe." Had this man really claimed to be the Christ? His mind turned back to his childhood, to the stories of the One who would come, who would restore the kingdom. He started to snort at the idea, the same reaction he had always expressed toward these crackpots who claimed to be the Messiah, but he stopped short. Perhaps it was right; this man was no lunatic. He felt toward this man much as a soldier feels toward a captain who he knows is braver and stronger than he; this man was master of the pain, He must be someone exceptional. The more he thought on it, the more he felt like believing that He could indeed be the Christ. But dying? The Chosen One dying?

And yet there was a certain fitness to the idea. He had seen enough of Palestine, he had known enough Romans and heard enough of their power to feel fairly confident that no one, be he ever so able as an organizer and leader, no one could conquer them. If the kingdom were to be set up in spite of this world-ruling power, it would almost have to be done by someone with supernatural powers. Perhaps this man had power over death, perhaps He would rise from the dead invincible, and go forth conquering and to conquer. It was not a very likely thought; but this pain was not very likely either, and the way that man was bearing it was even more unlikely.

The man at the far right had evidently been roused by that last derisive shout, and he, too, joined in, forcing out words so thick with bitterness and hate that they were almost palpable. "Are you not the Christ? Save yourself and us!"

His pain disappeared as the anger flared up in him at the words. The world grew red before his eyes, and he struggled in vain to free himself, oblivious of the pain. How could that man be so blind, how could he ignore the torture and the courage of the only innocent man of the three? He shouted out in a voice full of rage, "Do you not fear God, when you are suffering the same punishment? We, however, are suffering justly; we are getting our deserts for our misdeeds; but He has done nothing amiss." He slumped back against the cross, his strength gone because of the effort of speaking, but his mind was still seething with anger. His bitterness against the injustice of life welled up again in him. He was being rightly punished: he had known the risks of breaking the law, he had taken the chance and gotten caught. But was it right for him to have to take the chance in the first place? Did life have to be so one-sided? Was it impossible for the little people, the poor, the unfortunate to live without lying and cheating and stealing? Perhaps this man was the Christ; perhaps He would come back from the grave and set up His kingdom. But what good would that be if He followed the same pattern all the kingdoms had followed? He might succeed in setting up a kingdom, but it could not possibly be a righteous or just or even good kingdom if He forgot the downtrodden, if He did not do something — anything — for the people who were caught in this awful dilemma of wanting to live righteously but being unable to because of the injustice and capriciousness of life. There would be no point in any new kingdom if it forgot the people who, like himself, were pushed to the wall.

He raised his head and looked directly at the man — the Christ? — on his right. With all the feeling and passion he possessed, with all the compassion for those who were caught as he had been all his life, he said, "Jesus, remember me when you come into your kingdom!" It was not a personal request; his pain was so great that the only thing he could possibly desire was death, and he knew that would come soon enough. He knew that there was no hope for him but Sheol, and he had long since reconciled himself to that prospect, which was not undesirable even if it was not desirable. But he was thinking of those whom he had known, of all the countless downtrodden like him, of those whom this power-mad age ignored. If Jesus, too, ignored them, forgot them, He would not be the Messiah but a mockery. This Jesus must remember him, the man who had died beside Him, died for his own sins he was forced to commit; He must, He had to make some provision in His kingdom to insure that the same scene would not have to be repeated over and over and over.

He continued to look at the man next to him, and his vision was beginning to go black from exhaustion when the man turned His head and for the first time he saw His full face. It was flecked and streaked with blood and spittle, anything but a handsome sight. The man spoke: "I assure you," Jesus paused, gathering His breath, evidently finding speech as difficult as he had, "today you will be with Me in paradise!"

For an instant he did not understand the words, then he was stunned. Paradise? Not Sheol? Did He mean that, would He take him to some real, actual Paradise, rather than the place of the shades? What else could He have meant? He had said, "today," and they both knew that this was the day of death. He must have meant that; perhaps His kingdom was to be one designed specifically for

him and those like him, a place in which all the wrongs
of a world ruled by sin would be righted, where what
a person wanted and believed would mean more than what
life forced him to do, where a person would not have
to pay the penalty of his own shortcomings. Was He
actually setting up that sort of kingdom? Had He made
a way for men to be forgiven? The thought took his breath
away: for what other reason was this man, this Son of
God suffering if not for the sins of others? Had not the
guard said that He was being executed on hollow, trumped
up charges? He was not convicted for His own wrongs;
for whose, then? For everyone's?

He knew that the thought was incredible, absurd, and
yet his whole being reached out to it. His very soul cried
out, "This is Truth, the Truth. Believe in it, oh, believe
in it!" And he realized that he did believe in it, that all
his life he had been waiting and searching and groping
for this very answer, for this very man. A delicious peace
came over him, a peace the like of which he had never
before experienced. His pain was still present, still as intense, but somehow he felt as though it was no longer
such a trial to be endured, he felt as though its burden
had been lifted from him and another load had been put
in its stead, a load of peace and joy that covered and blotted
out the pain. It was still there, his hands and his feet and
his mouth and his muscles hurt just as much, but somehow
he was no longer suffering. Tears came to his eyes and
spilled over on to his cheeks and into his beard, tears partly
of joy and relief, and partly of an emotion he could not
name, an emotion brought forth by the knowledge that
Jesus, next to him, was even now suffering the torment
he had been and should still be suffering. Hanging on the

cross, in a world filled and overflowing with pain, he was a happier man than he had ever been before.

The rest of the afternoon passed swiftly for the thief. For three hours there was blessed darkness, darkness which he could drink in like icewater after the blistering heat, darkness which he could enjoy while the man next to him suffered all alone and in silence. He was humbled, he was awed by it, yet he was filled to the brim with a peace and contentment that nothing could mar. It was a drowsy, wonderful afternoon for him, and he welcomed the soldiers when at last they came to break his legs and let him die in a final paroxysm of pain. His last thoughts as they approached were of the words of his new-found Master. Soon they would meet, not nailed side by side to two crosses, but face to face. And if this Jesus could make even a cross so sweet, what would His Paradise be!

7
The Demon

7

The Demon

He then goes out to bring along with him seven other spirits worse than himself and they enter . . . .

THE *demons were near!*

It was very, very dark. The tiny group of women had to feel their way through the pre-dawn blackness. There was not a light, not a sound; the whole earth was standing on tiptoe. Mary Magdalene was leading the way, for only she and the other Mary had been that way before. Her face, could it have been seen, was drawn and tight with the grief of the past two days, but her mind was working at a fever pitch, it was clear as crystal. She recognized every bush that brushed by, she knew where every turn was, she knew just where the path went. She knew what she was doing.

The rest of the women thought they knew what she was doing. She had awakened each of them, had told them that it was time. Unquestioning, each of the women had gotten up, bringing with them the spices which they had mixed at Mary's suggestion, spices which they had mixed with their own tears during the endless, bleak Sabbath. This was the natural thing to do, the right thing to do; they would give to Jesus this last pitiful honor of a decent burial. Not as though it could atone for the unfairness of His trial, or for the ultimate of ignominies, the torture of a criminal's death, but because it was all they could do in protest to the brutal injustice of the Master's

end. This was what the rest of the women thought Mary
Magdalene was doing.

All except the other Mary. She did not know what
Mary Magdalene was doing. The day before, the Sabbath,
when Mary Magdalene was bidding the other women to
prepare the burial spices and was busily preparing them
herself, this Mary had tried to talk to her, tried to find out
just what she was up to. Not openly, though: it was not
the sort of time when you could bear talking to more than
one other who felt as you did, felt as though the bottom
had dropped out of everything, felt the gray mist of hopelessness all about where once there had been nothing but
radiance. For what Magdalene was doing made no sense,
none at all. For the other women, yes, it was the expected
thing, the correct thing to do. But not for Mary Magdalene.
For she and the other Mary had been at the tomb at dusk
on Friday, had seen Joseph laboring up the hill with his
burden that had late been their Lord, had seen Nicodemus
close behind, a little man seeming all the smaller because
of the great load of burial spices he was struggling to bring.
They had watched while the two men had wrapped His
body with the spices and the linen, had given Him His
burial. So Mary did not understand at all what Mary
Magdalene was doing, for what more could the women
do when the men had already buried Jesus? Yet when she
had broached the subject to her, Mary Magdalene had
turned on her with one look of such ferocious intensity
that Mary had instantly closed her mouth. She would
wait and see what would come to pass.

But Mary Magdalene knew what she was doing. She
was going to give her Jesus a proper burial. That it had
already been done did not bother her in the least. Jesus
was her Lord; she had been the one who cared for Him

during His short, turbulent ministry, she had been the one
who was with Him the whole time, she had been the one
who had not deserted Him. In death as in life, Jesus was
her Lord, not another's. Who was grieving as she was?
Whom did His death cut so deeply as it did her? Her
grief knew no limits; her grief was swelling up and closing
in about her moment by moment; her grief was becoming
and would always be her entire life. So one thing remained:
She must give to the Lord His burial, not because it would
help or hinder His corpse, not because it had or had not
been done already, but because it would seal Him for all
time as her dead Master, Mary Magdalene's. It would
make her grief a rightfully personal and unique possession.
Mary Magdalene knew what she was doing: she was lay-
ing claim to the right to grieve for her Lord. She would not
share that right.

They were almost at the tomb, with but one more bend
in the path and then the little hill. Suddenly there was a
jolt as the earth trembled beneath them, there was the
ominous grumbling as the earth settled, then quaked again.
The women stood stock still, huddling together in the
darkness. But when the earthquake had ceased Mary Magdalene started off toward the tomb without a word, and
the other women followed, all silent, all wondering what
this meant. As they approached the last bend in the path,
they could see a faint glow up ahead, and it brought a
shudder of awe. Mary Magdalene went on without so much
as hesitating, she rounded the bend and climbed the little
rise. She could see the tomb. But what she saw she could
not comprehend.

The demons were closer now, at the very gates.

A wonder, a miracle must have happened. A strange
light was streaming from the cave, and in the light the

women could see the prostrate forms of a half dozen men in guard uniforms. There had been a rumor that the Sanhedrin had posted a guard at the tomb, but here they were, unconscious on the ground. And even more wondrous, the huge stone which had been blocking the tomb lay to one side, its seal broken. The women hesitatingly lifted their eyes to the tomb, they saw the shrouds lying in order where Jesus had been laid, and they saw two men. Their appearance was like lightning, their garments white as snow — they were angels of the Lord. A thrill of excitement went through the women as simultaneously each recognized them as angels. They heard in the stunned silence of shock the words the angel said, "Have no fear! I know you are looking for Jesus who was crucified. He is not here; for He is risen, just as He said. Come, see the place where He lay. And go, hasten to tell His disciples, 'He is risen from the dead, and is preceding you into Galilee; there you will see Him.' See, I have told you."

There was a moment of silence. Then, with a suddenness that left them breathless, the women understood what he had said. The Lord was risen! The Lord was alive again! In a rush of joyous confusion the women turned and ran down the path in the dim light of the breaking day. Their thoughts were a tumult of joy and excitement.

All except Mary Magdalene. She trailed the rest by a bit, her face still the mask of grief. She, like them, had heard the words of the angel, she had heard them and started to understand them, then refused. The Lord was dead. She had seen Him die. She had entered into her grief, she would grieve the rest of her life for her Lord. The Lord was dead. With an effort of will she closed her mind tight against the words of the angel, she would not hear them, she could not understand them, perhaps she had misunderstood them, perhaps she did not hear them at all. Her walk was steady, her face grieving, her mind at peace. She was grieving for her Lord. Her Lord was dead. The other women were now chattering like excited magpies, but Mary was silent, silent and grieving, and feeling just the least bit superior to these addlepates who did not and could not share her burden of grief.

The women found the disciples. They had no trouble raising them, even though the sun was just making its appearance over the eastern hills, for none of them had slept much or soundly that weekend. They did not believe the excited women — who would have — and Mary Magdalene felt the hot flush of the conqueror as the superiority began to grow when the men shared her disdain for the silly misunderstanding of the other women.

Peter and John came out of the house, and, motioning them a bit to one side, away from the chattering women, Mary Magdalene told them in tones of a confidante, "They have taken away the Lord out of the sepulchre, and we know not where they have laid Him."

She offered to lead them to the tomb, and, since few were acquainted with that section of the city which served as the burial place of the rich, they followed her. When they came to the final bend in the path, Mary told them that the cave was not a hundred yards farther, and both the men began to run. Mary continued her steady walk, the slow walk of the mourner.

When she arrived at the tomb, they were already inside, and she stood at the entrance, enjoying the gentle luxury of letting the hot tears well up, filling her eyes and running on down her cheeks. She saw but did not notice them come out, Peter with a look of perplexity, but John with a face radiant enough to remove the slightest doubt that he believed. Mary continued to weep, a pitiable sight indeed, but inside she was exultant with a forever-to-be-hidden jubilance. Her Lord was dead, and she was in mourning. The others were not in mourning any longer, and that was all the better, for now no one would share her grief. She rested secure in grief, knowing that she would always grieve, that for the rest of her life she would move with delicate slowness, her body racked with deep sighs of hopelessness, her garments drab and her expression locked in lines of sorrow, knowing that hereafter and for the rest of her life people would come to her and they, too, would be moved by such a pitiable sight, that whenever her name was mentioned people would have a soft word, a pitying word for her, that even when her back was turned she could be sure that people would be looking at her and talking of her, knowing that she would never again have to suffer the chagrin of being seen for herself but could hide forever behind the bittersweet ambrosia of grief — safe, secure, untouched hereafter by the barbs and pains of life.

For Mary's mind had turned inward. She was no longer interested in Jesus for Himself; she had taken her own memories and made an idol of them. She had taken her own wishes and desires, her own selfishness, and had made a graven image. And she had taken her idol, named it "Jesus," and prostrated herself before the altar of Self. Her will was now her God; blind selfishness reigned supreme. Clothed in the vestments of outward grief, she would spend the rest of her days exacting from others the gratification of her own egotism, her own desire to be pitied, to receive sympathy.

Mary stood without the tomb weeping, but her heart

was exuberant. She stooped down for one last look into the
tomb of her dead Lord.

The demons were entering the very tabernacle.

The mind is easily trained. The same two angels were
there, but Mary did not recognize them, for she had convinced herself that the first episode was a chimera and had
never really happened. So taut was her self-imposed blind-
ness of eye and mind that this time she did not even have to
be bothered with the uncomfortable realization that they
were angels. There was a look of bewilderment on their
faces, and they asked in tones of surprise and wonder,
"Woman, why are you crying?" and they emphasized "you"
just as if to add "of all people." But Mary serenely ignored
the emphasis of the question — to answer that would have
invited disaster — and replied in tones most piteous and
heart rending, "Because they have taken away my Lord,
and I do not know where they have placed Him." Before
the angels could answer (and she secretly feared what they
might tell her) she turned around and saw Jesus.

*The demons had almost conquered, they had a definite
advantage.*

A small part of her mind, that infinitesimal fraction that
had not yet been swallowed by the insanity of grief,
screamed within her, causing her pulse to quicken, her
body to grow rigid with tension. That part of her mind
recognized her Lord. But only for an instant. Then, like
a juggernaut, her grief suppressed this threat, it stamped
the thought down into the very dust with the firm, un-
shakeable resolve that she would grieve, she would grieve,
she would grieve; her Lord was dead. And the danger
passed. Her mind closed back in on itself, it began to work
faster and faster in the channel that brought comfort,
moment by moment her mind shut itself to the reality of

the actual world in favor of the delicious if slightly intoxicating incense of her inner world of grief. Her mind was in complete control now, it ruled as tyrant unchallenged. She did not recognize Jesus, in spite of her more than two years in intimate association with Him, in spite of the fact that He stood not ten feet from her (and by now the sun was well above the horizon), in spite of the fact that her eyes presented to her mind the familiar countenance. (Tears may blur, but they never blind.)

Confident now that no threat could mar her sublime grief, she presumed that He was the gardener, she spoke with the tremulous voice of the deeply distressed, "Sir, if you have carried Him off, tell me where you have put Him, and I will remove Him."

Jesus said to her, "Mary!" and He did not say it in the soothing tones of a mother lulling a fretful child to sleep. The voice of Jesus was the peal of thunder as the fire of God came down to the earth, it was the crash of the Red Sea as it swallowed up Pharaoh, it was the shout of a half million people as the walls of Jericho fell, it was the voice of the Almighty that melted the earth; it was the slap in the face of the hysterical woman. The voice of Jesus shook the entire being of Mary Magdalene, it hit her like a giant fist of steel, it snapped her eyes wide open and shattered the shell with which she had very nearly enveloped herself. She fell at His feet and sobbed, "Rabboni!"

Mary had seen the face of the demons. Mary had seen herself.

8
The Doubter

8

The Doubter

"Let us go, too, so that we may die with Him."

EVERY true story teems with people who are not really there. These are the shadow people, the supporting cast, the men who stood just to one side of the hero, and whom history has all but forgotten. The disciple Thomas was one of these furtive, hidden people. Overshadowed by the grandeur of his Master we come across him now and again as we leaf through the pages of the gospels. We seldom see Thomas full face; usually he is present only by implication, when the Twelve are referred to. Occasionally we come across his direct footprints, as in the lists of the apostles when he is mentioned by name. Only on a few occasions do we see Thomas front and center, rather than among the shrubbery and buildings of the backdrop.

Even from such a paucity of pictures we can make out much of the real Thomas. For one thing, we may infer that Thomas did not possess a magnetic personality — if he had, we might have seen more of him. Thomas was not what one would call popular. He was probably one of the cynical, slightly bitter people; he was a man most of us would avoid.

But a few of the gifted are able to see beneath such cynicism (certainly Jesus did), and what they see does much to compensate for the discordant outward finish. What they see is a person who actually wants to be loved, a rather

99

34401

emotional person, who once had (and, down deep, still has) the frank, open, puppydog warmth of a little boy. Thomas was one of these people, and as we shall see, that was precisely why he struck most men as a cynic. For life, then as now, does not always treat such warmth tenderly.

We have no direct evidence, but we may certainly infer that Thomas was a man who bore the scars of life: he had been hurt, and not infrequently. Perhaps his parents had been unable to return his love, or perhaps death or the Romans had separated them from him too early. Perhaps a warm and affectionate yearning for God had been trodden down by a Pharisaism chilled in its creed. Perhaps love unrequited had left its wounds time and again, or perhaps causes that caught the fire of youthful idealism had turned to ashes in the face of stern reality. Perhaps even the nickname "Twin" was a constant reopening of a never-to-heal wound that ought to lie buried in a forgotten memory.

We have no direct evidence. The gospels leave Thomas' past in shrouds of silence. And doubtless the evangelists knew little more of his past than we, for one who has been hurt repeatedly learns that to bare himself even to friends is to invite further pain. He learns to raise a protective barrier, to crouch behind the safety that cynicism and outward bitterness afford, to remain detached and aloof, to avoid emotional entanglement by criticizing instead of praising, by giving advice instead of encouraging.

But the Master saw through the facade to the man beneath, the man who needed Him. And He set about drawing forth the Thomas that was hiding there. The first time we meet Thomas face to face we see the wonder of a real, warm love breaking out from the safe comfort of introverted seclusion into the dangerous no man's land of leadership.

Jesus had determined to go to Jerusalem. His journeys and His preaching of many, many months had aroused religious and political enmity to a fever pitch, yet in spite of this Jesus was going to come out of the anonymity of the up-country into the perilous publicity of the capital. The disciples were of one voice in their argument, doing their best to persuade Jesus that for His own good He must not go now.

To no avail. Jesus had set His face toward Jerusalem. Then, cutting through the silence with a razor keenness often found only in the sensitive man, Thomas struck the disciples' Achilles' tendon. The disciples were actually less worried about Jesus' safety than their own. There was no real answer to Thomas' "Let us go, too, so that we may die with Him." It is significant that Thomas, the reserved, the critic, who never dared act on impulse, was the first to be ready to die with Jesus. The months and months of the Master's love had won; Thomas, the cynic, had broken out through the shell, had thrown caution to the winds. He had given his love to Jesus.

But he had not given it completely. A fortnight or so later, after Jesus had raised Lazarus, after the triumphal entry, at the close of the almost unbearably wonderful intimacy of the Last Supper, we meet Thomas again. It was in the Upper Room, and Jesus had been trying to get over to their clouded intellects the fact that He must go to prepare a place for them, when Thomas interrupted: "Lord, we do not know where you are going; how do we know the way?"

Do we detect here a note of the old cynicism? Was Thomas unconsciously criticizing this riddle talk? Or is there a hint of bitterness here? Was Thomas' love for Jesus yet tainted by the fear that past injury had produced? Did Thomas yet distrust the Lord, did he have misgivings that

Jesus was going to leave him comfortless as many, many others had? Perhaps. Or perhaps not. John did not know (though he may have guessed), for he recorded the question without comment. It may have been merely that Thomas wanted to exclude the possibility of Jesus going off without realizing that he was ready to go with Him, wherever.

At any rate, there can be little doubt at our third meeting with Thomas. Jesus, the one who drew Thomas out, had been crucified. Thomas, who secretly knew all along that it would happen like this, had hoped against hope, and had seen his hope shattered. A part of Thomas died with Jesus, that part that ever could dare to love again.

We meet Thomas as the other ten have told him in excited jubilance that they have seen the Lord. Thomas, his cynical old self again, bites off his words as he tells them, "Unless I see in his hands the print of the nails and put my finger in the mark of the nails and thrust my hand in his side, I will not at all believe." The disciples, after a moment or so, shrug the hard, shock-intending reply off with an epithet that was trite before it was ever spoken: "Doubting Thomas."

Except, perhaps, for John. Perhaps John, who recorded the incident, who knew more of love than most men, saw the tears that were aching to well up into the cold, cynical eyes, saw the teeth that were drawing blood from the cheek, saw the tortured, miserable, wretched soul writhing and turning this way and that but finding no shelter from pain. Perhaps John understood that the grim statement was a defense raised in desperation by a man who yearned more than anyone to believe but just could not face being hurt again.

For Thomas was dying inside. Never again would life

be able to offer anything to him, never would he be able to entrust himself to anyone, not even God. It was a dying man to whom Jesus came after eight days. Jesus came to meet a man aching to believe in Him, yet not daring He met Thomas on his own level, offering to give whatever evidence of His Resurrection Thomas needed. And Thomas' answer, "My Lord and my God!" is the evidence of a miracle taken place, the cry of release of one who never needs to fear being hurt again, because he has met the One whose love can fill all the gaps, can heal all the wounds caused by experience however bitter, can never fail because He has conquered death.

The other disciples did not understand this. They continued to think of Thomas as the doubter, the cynic, the stern, self-righteous unbeliever who had to be shown. Perhaps it was lost on John; and yet one would expect that if he did comprehend, a man who knew love so intimately would write the story with a consummate delicacy that would be understood only by those who have experienced deep emotions.

We do not know what became of Thomas. Once he went fishing with Peter and the rest; perhaps he remained in Palestine. Perhaps the legends are true, and after Pentecost he went to Egypt or Illyricum or even India. But whether he stayed in Jerusalem or went to Cathay and the ends of the earth, we may rest assured that the Christ gave him His personal Great Commission when He said, "Blessed are those who believe without seeing." For the rest of his life Thomas was seeking out those who, like him, had been hurt too often, had been disappointed too many times to give themselves again to anyone or anything, even though the yearning to love and be loved at times reached an unbearable crescendo. To these, to the bitter, to the ones trembling deep behind a desperate fortress of cynicism, unwilling to believe because afraid of the bitter anguish of more disappointment, Thomas preached the good news that the love of Jesus binds all wounds, never disappoints, that the thirsting soul need not reject Him from the fear of being hurt again, for His is the unspeakable comfort of a love that overflows and overflows, clear on into the dim corridors of all the ages yet to be. This was what Thomas preached.

And he never stopped. Thomas may be only lurking in the shadows of the gospels, but to those who listen he preaches still. He preaches today.

9
The Diplomat

9

The Diplomat

"You stiff-necked and uncircumsised of heart and ear . . . ."

MANY and varied as are the reasons men require before they will act, they are usually traceable to the make-up of the man himself. Often reason will dictate, or sometimes a man may act because of the promptings of his conscience. But occasionally there will appear a prophet or a man of God whose actions will be the result of another force, a force which has its origin elsewhere than the man's intellect or background or habit patterns. Stephen is a case in point.

One of the first problems to arise in the early church was the dispute over the distribution to the widows. When the Greek Christians complained that their widows were being slighted, the apostles, rather than burden themselves with administrative chores, proposed that deacons be chosen. Seven men were elected to supervise the allocation of the common goods, and surprisingly (although it really shouldn't be surprising) all were Greeks. Here Stephen's name appears for the first time. Evidently he was looked up to by the other Christians not only for his fairness, but, even more important in an administrator, because he knew how to execute right decisions without alienating those who disagreed with him. The Early Church had all things in common; in such a situation there are bound to be those who disagree with the apportionment of the goods. The church would certainly not elect a man to be deacon who did not have the ability to win others to his point of view.

That Stephen had this talent became even more apparent
in the days that followed. Stephen knew men, he knew well
the techniques of persuasion. So eloquent did he become
that no man could withstand him. There is an art to force-
ful debate: Not only does it require logical acuity, the
ability to strike to the center of the problem, but it also
requires that other talent, the almost instinctive knowledge
of what things are most important to the listeners. Logic
must be coupled with persuasion; when the two are wed,
then indeed one finds a man whose argument attracts attention.

And in practically no time at all, Stephen did attract
attention. No man can win over to his side all his hearers,
and it was not long before the hard core of Pharisaism had
been sufficiently angered by his arguments to bring him
to trial for heresy. And it was here, before the council, that
Stephen began to do just the opposite of what would be
expected of a man like him. For the defense he made was
by no means a masterpiece of logical persuasion. He started
with the theme that God was not localized to any particular
place, that He had spoken time and again outside of the
Holy Land. This was no impregnable argument, at least not
to the scribes and lawyers. Any one of them could have
claimed (falsely, perhaps, but forcefully) that Stephen was
misinterpreting, that in each case God was speaking in
order to lead the people to the place He had chosen.
Stephen was on trial; how could he choose as his defense
an argument so palpably vulnerable as this?

Even using such an argument, Stephen could perhaps
have won his case by a masterful presentation of it. But
he did not; his presentation was absurd. Stephen laboriously
spelled out every detail of his illustrations. He could not
have been unaware that each member of the council knew

Israel's history from memory, and yet, choosing the four or five most famous events, events which a word or a phrase would have identified, he went into each one in such detail as to lose completely whatever point he was making. Any orator knows that when his audience has already heard what he is saying, he has lost his audience. Minds wander, fingers drum, and sheer boredom follows close on the heels of the triteness. Yet even this mistake was not insurmountable; if Stephen, realizing that he had gone too far in detailing the obvious, had recovered himself after the first illustration, he still could have brought brilliance to the other examples. But he did not; interminably he continued to dwell on the minute, repeating over and again what the newest proselyte would have known by rote. An argument that bores is already lost.

But Stephen was not content with being a bore; he was a standing insult to the intelligence of the Sanhedrin. Stephen was a Greek; here, on trial before Jerusalem's highest court, he must have been doubly aware of his alien upbringing. And the council knew it, too, from his accent if nothing else. Yet he had the audacity to stand before the very leaders of Israel, men whose entire lives had been steeped in the tradition and history of the Jews, and he, a Jew of the dispersion, had the gall to lecture them on their own history. What effect could he hope to have on them? He acted almost as though he were trifling with them.

Such boring presumptuousness would have been bad enough. But then, having already alienated his listeners, he made the mistake of attacking the Temple. And this was indeed a mistake. Though there were doubtless hypocrites on the council, men whose only interest was self aggrandizement and the income the Temple attracted, it is unjust to suppose that there were no honest men on that high body. Certainly there were some (perhaps even a majority) who were sincerely seeking to do what was right, who were willing to give even Stephen a fair hearing; Gamaliel had shown such an attitude, and even though he did not agree with the Christians, was willing to let time be their judge. For such men the Temple symbolized all that was good, all that was holy. The Temple was the center of their worship, and they were sincerely (if wrongly) seeking to worship God. It was also the symbol of their deep love for their people, the sign of all their nationalistic aspirations. The Temple was the symbol they held dear above all others, and yet Stephen slapped them in the face by attacking it. Stephen was no ignoramus; he knew that he was sowing the wind by attacking the Temple.

And then, as if to insure that he would reap the whirl-wind, he broke off in the middle of his speech and, at the top of his voice, called them the worst names he could think of. He called them stiffnecked, uncircumcised killers. Murderers. Technically he may have been correct; they had crucified Jesus illegally. But Peter had already charged them with that; they were not ignorant of that infraction. If there is anything worse than accusing a man of a crime he did not commit, it is to accuse him of a crime he knows that he did commit. Stephen, after all, was not the judge at this trial. He was on trial for his life and for his beliefs. In a sense he was on trial as a representative of Christianity. Even if the other mistakes he made in his defense could be ascribed to mere ineptness, this could not be. What was Stephen doing?

Actually, Stephen did not know what he was doing. An ignoramus could perhaps have blindly committed these unforgivable errors, but Stephen was an elected official of the church. A thoroughgoing egotist could perhaps have excused such mistakes, but Stephen had met his Master. Stephen certainly was aware of what was happening, he recognized and no doubt was appalled by what he was doing. Yet there are times when conscience and reason both have to bow to a mightier force. Stephen, all through his defense, had felt absolute assurance that he was being led by the Spirit of God, that it was not he who was speaking but the Spirit of the Father speaking in him. He had felt as the prophets of old had felt, when the Holy Spirit took complete possession of their lives, when they burned with the words God wanted spoken. His intellect had been protesting, his conscience had been screaming that this wasn't right, wasn't what he should be saying, and yet both reason and conscience had been nullified by the power of what Stephen felt was the Spirit of God.

And it must have been God's Spirit which directed his fatal defense. His outburst had been too much for his audience; they rushed him outside the gates to be stoned. There, while they paused, Stephen had the opportunity to reverse their decision. The majority of the council were men of some integrity; certainly as they stood there, feeling the black passion of the mob that had gathered, they must have reflected a bit. Reason must have gained the upper hand over their anger, and one sentence of sense from Stephen would have been enough to make them reconsider.

But just at that moment, Stephen burst out with the final indignity: "I see the heavens opened, and the Son of Man standing at God's right hand." That sealed his fate. How can we explain that statement? Perhaps Stephen made it up: but would he, a deacon of the new church, resort to an open lie, especially when his life was hanging in the balance? Perhaps it was an hallucination: but would God desert a servant of His at such a time? Would He not at least have kept Stephen from disclosing such a catastrophic hallucination? The only reasonable answer must be that God had indeed been directing his defense, that God Himself had led Stephen to the point of martyrdom and then had granted to him a vision of such magnitude that Stephen could not remain silent. And the vision was enough to sentence him, finally and inexorably.

For God did want Stephen to be His martyr. There were things that needed to be accomplished, and there was no other way to bring them to pass. Saul, remember, was a witness, and immediately afterward he embarked on the course of persecution which led him to his conversion. But the conversion of Saul the persecutor to Paul the missionary was only an incidental result of Stephen's martyrdom.

The real reason for Stephen's death was the persecution that followed it. "And at that time a severe persecution broke out against the church in Jerusalem; so that all except the apostles were dispersed over Judean and Samaritan communities." Jesus had commissioned them when He left the earth, He had given them their charge. "But you will receive power, when the Holy Spirit comes upon you, and you will be My witnesses both in Jerusalem and in all Judea and in Samaria and to the remotest end of the earth." The Jerusalem church had prospered; it was now some five thousand strong. Yet with all its size and with all the apostolic power that was available to it, it had not yet shown any interest whatsoever in missionary activity. It was content to remain there with no thought whatsoever of the millions beyond Jerusalem who were hungering and thirsting to hear the good news, to learn that Jesus had died for all men, everywhere. The church was lethargic; although it was growing by leaps and bounds, it was stagnant and fruit-less. The only way they were at last stirred out of their complacency was by the persecution, which forced them to go into all the world. And Stephen was God's instrument to bring about that persecution.

Stephen's defense was inexcusable. He was intelligent enough to know that what he was doing was the very opposite of what he should have done, his conscience was telling him all along that his speech was not loving, was not charitable, was not even diplomatic. And yet, when Stephen recognized the voice of the Spirit of God, he was willing to abandon himself to Him, to hold nothing back from following the Lord where He was leading. Because it was necessary for him to be sacrificed. Stephen certainly did not foresee the results of his death; he did not know why the Lord was leading him that way. But he knew that the Lord was leading him.

And it was enough.

10
The Missionary

10

The Missionary

He had four virgin daughters who prophesied.

PHILIP died at a good old age, full of years, and was gathered to his people. His daughters did not mourn him — they loved him too much for that; they understood. For the rest of time, Christians would remember him as Philip the Evangelist. He could have been known as the Apostle to the Gentiles, and perhaps he knew it. But it did not matter.

Perhaps this was the special reason for his inviting Paul to stay with him on his way to Jerusalem. It may have been that Philip knew that Paul's fame and success could have been his. Perhaps Philip had always held a special sort of love for Paul, knowing that Paul would be remembered as the Great Missionary only because he, Philip, had deferred the honor.

More likely, however, Philip was unaware of the reason for his special fondness for Paul. With all justice, Philip could have loved Paul as a son, for had he not chosen to step down, Paul would always have followed in his footsteps. But Philip was not the sort to be paternal with any of the brethren. Not because of any mawkish, self-effacing, false humility on his part, but because he just would not have realized that for a moment at least, the course of history rested on his decision. And if he had realized it, he probably would not have given it a second thought. That is true humility.

Philip was a rare man, a great man, an unknown man.

117

Unknown because of his greatness. There are those who remain unknown through cowardice; Philip was not one of them. Occasionally, though, there is a man who chooses to be unknown. In Philip was the rare combination of striking personal leadership and deep, absolute humility. Seldom is such a combination encountered. Had he lived in a later age, Philip would have been called a mystic, for in him were combined all the dynamic qualities of the prophets of old, with total surrender to his God. He walked in a supernatural, intensely personal relationship with his Lord.

In other words, Philip was a Christian. The first mention of him in Scripture is in the list of the seven deacons appointed by the church. In the light of what his later actions reveal of him, it is easy to see why he was elected to this position of responsibility. For one thing, he was a man of zeal, one who could be counted upon to carry out a given task to the best of his ability. For another, he was selfless in the best sense of the word, caring not at all for himself. But most important, he was a devout man, one who walked with God.

It was in the persecution which followed Stephen's death, when the Christians were forced to flee from Jerusalem, that his greatness became evident. Philip went to a city of Samaria. This was a startling thing for him to do, for the Samaritans were emphatically hated by Judeans. They were outcasts, untouchables, gentiles of the gentiles. Indeed, had not even Jesus as much as told the Samaritan woman that her people did not even know God? Before Philip could choose to go to Samaria with the Gospel, he had to think hard and clearly, he had to see through the prejudice and racial hatred of Judea, he had to understand the gentle irony in his Master's statement.

His choice to go to Samaria was a choice that would mark an epoch. So far as we know, Philip was the first to free himself from the confines of an exclusively national Jewish sentiment and carry the Gospel to others, who were not of the erstwhile true faith. Philip opened the door to the gentiles, he was the first to preach Christ to the gentiles.

His evangelistic efforts were of no little success. The entire village accepted his good news. Some years later, Peter was to preach to a gentile centurion and then use the incident as *ex post facto* evidence to gain gentile admission among the Jerusalem Christians. Philip could have done the same thing, not with a mere household to support the claim, but with an entire city. But he chose not to. God had blessed Philip's work, made it prosper to such an extent that Philip certainly could rightfully have claimed a position of great leadership in the church. But Philip had no need of such a position; his was the true humility that has no need of self aggrandizement, for all his wishes and ambitions were already fulfilled in his Lord.

Instead, Philip waited patiently until the Jerusalem church sent Peter and John to confirm his ministry. Not that his work needed confirmation; the Spirit of God had already confirmed it, with signs and wonders such as to amaze even a professional sorcerer. When Peter and John arrived, Philip retired without a word, he gave to them the privilege of taking the lead. Philip deferred to them in spite of the fact that it had been his ministry which had brought the people to believe, it had been his mighty works which had confounded the superstition and witchcraft which had clouded the people's minds. Philip had the gift of selflessness; his joy at the work of Peter and John was fully as great as any joy he could have gained through his own work.

But it would seem that he was chosen for leadership,

in spite of himself. In the mysterious subjectivity of his communion with God, he heard the command to go south, to meet a man on the Gaza road. There he met the eunuch of Candace. This man was an Ethiopian, an African Negro. If there had been any doubts in Philip's mind about the fact that he was being called to the gentiles, they could remain no longer. He might have made a weak case for the fact that at one time the Samaritans were part of the people of Israel, and thus they really were in some sense under the Covenant. But with the eunuch, there could be no such rationalizing, for he was not only a foreigner, he was manifestly a foreigner. Yet Philip did not hesitate; he accepted the challenge and preached Christ to this gentile. The ready acceptance which met his message could leave no doubt that his opportunities for evangelizing a world hungry for the Christ were unlimited.

We are told that "the Lord's Spirit hurriedly transported Philip, and the eunuch did not see him any more." The very least that this enigmatic statement could mean is that now Philip was especially close to his God, that now he was at the acme of transcendental fellowship with the Infinite. He could not possibly have doubted that the Lord was pleased with his preaching to the gentiles.

We next find him at Azotus, a village on the Mediterranean coast, on the road that goes from Syria to Egypt. Here he had to make his choice. He could choose to go south. The road led from Azotus to Gaza, on the border of Palestine, and then on to Egypt. He could head south to the learned center of Alexandria, south to the fertile farmlands of the Nile, which supplied the grain for the Roman Empire, south to the centers of commerce which joined two great continents. He could choose to go south, to be the leader of the vanguard of Christianity as it spread

from Jerusalem to cover the face of the earth. He was offered the inestimable privilege of being the Apostle to the
Gentiles, the one responsible for bringing the good news
to all the Christendom of the future.

To the north, the road led back to Palestine. If Philip
went north, he must turn his back on the clear and definite
call to begin a vast missionary enterprise. He must give
up the fame and glory, he must specifically refuse that
high calling of God, he must let the world wait for another
to mould its destiny.

Philip went north.

A mistake, a tragedy! Philip could have been great, he
could have been a hero of history, but he chose to be insignificant. To Paul must pass the laurel, Paul, whose theo-
logical brilliance would bring him more than enough fame
for one man, Paul, whose zeal and ability would win him
a place of predominance whatever he did. Paul, then,
inherited by default the privilege of being the Missionary
to the Gentiles. But even worse, Philip not only gave up
greatness, he specifically refused a clear calling of God,
he turned his back on a vocation the Lord had appointed
him for.

Opportunity comes to every man once. Every man has
one high calling from God, one vocation for which he
is especially fitted. Philip's talents qualified him for a
spectacular ministry in the van of triumphant Christianity.
And Philip missed his opportunity, he refused the call.
Not that he fled from the task, not that he was overwhelmed
by the difficulty of preaching. He preached in every village
on the road north, he settled in Caesarea, a trading center,
where there would always be a need for an evangelist. But
he missed his great call. Or so it would seem.

To some men, opportunity comes more than once. There

are two ways of looking at God's call. Most of us are of such limited ability that out of all the possible vocations, there is but one in which we can be useful. To us God gives one compelling call, and woe to us if we flee it. Perhaps this is due to our limited talents; yet the multitude of possible fields of service would make it seem that that is not the real reason that we have but one true vocation. Perhaps the real reason we have only one high calling is that we have not yet plumbed the depths of self surrender and divine love. If we had, we would know greatness, and to the great there is an infinite number of vocations.

Philip was a great man. Because he had given his multitude of talents to God in mystical, deep humility, Philip was given two choices. He could have had a career which offered so much that it would be excruciatingly tantalizing to anyone of less stature than he. But he had another choice, and that was the calling he devoted his life to. Philip chose to be insignificant, to take as his own a difficult, obscure work with the few who needed him in Caesarea. And it would be tantamount to blasphemy to assume that his choice was against the will of God.

To be sure, we lose sight of Philip. For twenty years he vanishes from the scene, swallowed up in the obscurity of a small, local ministry. And yet when his name reappears some twenty years later, we have no reason to assume that he was living in conflict with the will of God. He was still known as Philip the Evangelist. His children had grown up into the same mystical relationship with God that he had known. Obviously, God did not desert him, he did not flee from the face of God when he turned north instead of south.

And yet, as the years went by, and especially as he talked with Paul at the conclusion of his missionary suc-

cesses, Philip must have known that he could have had a
ministry different from the obscurity of his unexciting local
church. Doubtless he knew that he had made the choice
at Azotus. But he did not mourn a missed opportunity.
Those who have learned to walk in mysterious fellowship
with God never have cause to mourn. Had he gone south,
his life would have been rich and full of adventure and high
accomplishment. Instead, he turned north, and his life
had been rich and full of ministering to the needy, of the
warmth and closeness that only comes from children and
family, of mystical fellowship and exquisite love from God.

Philip was fully devoted to his Master, he had found
the true humility which self surrender gives. Because he
was a Christian in the finest sense, his calling was not a
single, only opportunity. The whole world lay before him;
he could choose any occupation, any direction, confident in
the assurance that whatever he did, he would not walk
alone. No area was closed to him, no road could possibly
exclude the love and fellowship of Almighty God. Whatever he chose, Philip would never have cause to mourn,
for his Master would fill his cup to overflowing wherever
he was. Philip had heard and understood his Master's
greatest promise: "Lo, I am with you alway, even unto the
end of the world."

Philip died at a good old age, full of years, and was
gathered to his people. His daughters did not mourn him —
they loved him too much for that; they understood. For
the rest of time, Christians would remember him as Philip
the Evangelist. He could have been known as the Apostle
to the Gentiles, and perhaps he knew it. But it did not
matter.

11
The Betrayer

11

The Betrayer

Lord, thou knowest all things; thou knowest that I love thee.

DAWN is always a bit exciting, when the promise of the light is at last fulfilled in the breathtaking person of the sun, when the plans and activities of the coming day are still shrouded in the stillness and calm left over from the night. On the Sea of Tiberius the heat that will later become oppressive is noticeable almost as soon as the sun has cleared the hills, but the mystery remains for a while nonetheless. Especially on that morning, the world seemed to have halted for an indefinite moment of breathless wonder.

Peter was still a little chilly, for even on a warm morning the fire feels good after an unexpected plunge into the lake. But as he finished the bread and fish, the last drops of water had dried and the warm good humor characteristic of him again was in complete possession. Or at least almost complete. Peter was still awed by the presence of his Master, awed and so inwardly ecstatic that he wished the enchantment would never be broken. He was not yet used to the fact that Jesus was alive, that though He had died He had conquered death. Peter's mind was not quick, and after having been thrown into such a turmoil by the death of Jesus, he was even slower in becoming accustomed to the scope of the victory which Jesus the Christ had won. True, he had seen Him before since the Resurrection, but each time the dream-like aura of the meetings had clouded his feelings so that he still felt a thrill of surprise and excitement when he looked at the Lord.

Seeing that everyone had finished breakfast, Jesus broke the spell by getting up and scuffing dirt over the coals of the fire. He stepped on the pile of dirt once or twice to make sure the fire was out, then stretched and sat back down cross-legged on the ground almost directly across from Peter. There was a strange, quizzical expression on His face, and He was looking directly into Peter's eyes. Finally He said, "Simon, son of Jonas, lovest thou me more than these?"

Peter was disturbed by the question. He was not puzzled so much by what the Lord was referring to when He said, "more than these," but he wondered why the Lord used that particular word for "love." In every conversation there are meanings that lie below the surface, meanings that find their expression not directly in words and definitions, but in vocal inflections and gestures and expressions, or even in the choice of one word instead of its more common synonym. The word that Jesus had chosen seemed strange to Peter, for it was a word that suggested admiration and respect and intellectual preference, but it did not seem to Peter to be a strong enough word for the way he felt toward his Master. So when he answered, "Yea, Lord, thou knowest that I love thee," he used a word which seemed to him far more meaningful, a word that implied boundless, inexhaustible love, a word teeming with overtones of the deepest sort of affection, an almost passionate word for love. Peter loved Jesus with his whole heart.

But Jesus' answer was merely, "Feed my lambs," and He looked troubled. He asked again, "Simon, son of Jonas, lovest thou me?" and this time He emphasized the word "love" — that same word, that lifeless, bloodless, almost academic word — and Peter again replied with the strongest word he knew to express his feelings. Jesus answered, "Feed my sheep," and His face carried an expression of such disappointment and sorrow that Peter wanted to cry out. He asked the question a third time, "Simon, son of Jonas, lovest thou me?" This time He used Peter's word.

Peter should have felt gratified, for Jesus was no longer asking him if he loved Him only rationally, platonically, in deliberateness of choice. But Peter was disturbed. He had heard that question before, that inflection that made it an almost rhetorical question, and he was still smarting from the sorrow that he had caused so soon after it. The night before Jesus had been crucified, He had asked Peter in exactly the same tones, "Wilt thou lay down thy life for my sake?" And then had followed the prediction that would never cease to haunt him, "Verily, verily I say unto thee, The cock shall not crow, till thou hast denied me thrice." Peter was grieved, for he knew that the Master was probing for something, something that He felt Peter was still lacking. But where there may have been doubts about his courage, Peter could not conceive any flaws in his love for Jesus. He loved Jesus in a way that utterly overwhelmed him, his love for this man was so great and deep and overpowering that it was like no other love he had ever experienced; even his love for his wife (and Peter loved his wife) seemed paltry and lackluster in comparison. It was inconceivable that Peter could love his Lord more; Peter loved Jesus entirely, with his whole being. That other time he may have been blustering, but this time he was not, and he was sure that Jesus knew that.

Yet the Lord was not satisfied, not at all. He said, "Feed my sheep," almost perfunctorily, and then followed with a prediction that sounded frighteningly like that other prediction. "Verily, verily, I say unto thee, When thou wast young, thou girdedst thyself, and walkedst whither thou wouldest: but when thou shalt be old, thou shalt stretch forth thy hands, and another shall gird thee, and carry thee whither thou wouldest not."

Peter's heart beat faster, for he saw as clearly as though it had been painted before him the cross that awaited him when he had finished his days. Yet he did not fear it; he had no question that he would shrink from it, for his love for Jesus was strong enough to lead him even to be crucified. Indeed, Jesus did not seem to be doubting that; He seemed to be driving at something else, something which eluded Peter's grasp. Why did Jesus predict his death when they had been talking of his love for Him? What was the connection? Peter wondered; even during the rest of the conversation he was wondering. Try as he might, he could not see what the one had to do with the other. It was a problem that would bother him for the rest of his life.

✻   ✻   ✻   ✻   ✻

The forenoon is a man's time, a time of action and ambition and accomplishment. During these hours, when energy is at its peak, worlds are shaken and empires are founded. In Jerusalem the mid-morning was a busy time, a time of activity in the not yet oppressive heat, when routine and boredom had not yet cloyed the day's tasks, when there were things to be done and this was the time to do them. Man is at his peak during the forenoon.

This was the beginning of a new era, and Peter was overwhelmed by it. Never had there been such preaching, and now not by one man or five, but by the whole crowd of them. All of the followers were there in the open market, and each was a John the Baptist. Now a man would speak with a voice of power in what sounded to Peter like Greek, now another in Latin, then two or three would preach almost together in a language Peter had never heard, and sure enough, a handful of men whose native tongue they were speaking would gather. Soon the whole area was filled with little clusters of men, with a disciple or two or three in the center of each group. Peter could not understand what they were saying — he was not a learned man — but he knew what their message was. For all of them at once had caught fire, they had even seen what appeared to be tongues of fire, and they had begun to burn with the message that Jesus was the Christ, the Anointed. The excitement was all but unbearable; Peter knew now how the prophets of old had felt, for this was the Spirit of God. He had come, not to a solitary figure, but to each of them, to all who believed in Jesus, and it was absolutely indescribable; none of them could contain themselves, they had to tell the whole city the good news.

Peter was not educated, but he knew the Scriptures. This was a sign of the kingdom, a sign that God's rule in absence would soon be done. A crowd of the curious soon collected near where Peter was standing, and Peter did not need even a moment's hesitation to answer their mocking insults. Peter called to them and preached a sermon whose power was a thing of awe. Peter was filled with the power of God, he knew just where he stood and that nothing was so powerful as the message of Jesus of Nazareth, God's King. His preaching had a thunder never before heard, a force that could not be resisted. It shook the soul of man and boy to the very core. Peter was invincible, the leader of a mighty deluge of the power of God.

And it did not end with the three thousand converts of Pentecost. As each day passed, Peter knew more and more of the Power. Wherever he went he saw men shaken

and conquered by the might of the Messiah, and wherever
he went, men knew that Peter was filled with the Spirit
of Almighty God. The power of God was the theme of
every sermon, every conversation; Peter was overwhelmed
by the exaltation of the King of Israel.

As the weeks passed, it became evident to the growing
community of Christians that Peter was at the front of the
movement. Peter had always been a leader; now, imbued
with the abundance of the Spirit of God, there was no question of whom God had chosen to lead the movement to
victory after victory. And Peter himself recognized that
God had chosen him as a special messenger of the power
of the Christ. He realized now what Jesus had meant on
that morning when He had told Peter to feed His sheep.

And yet it seemed strange to him. He seemed to himself the least qualified to feed the flock. Had not he be-
trayed the Lord? Had not he been tried and somehow been
found wanting on the question of love? Peter did not understand why the Lord had appointed him; and yet it could
not be disputed. Each day the power of the Christ became
more real and dynamic to him, and each day he grew to
love his Jesus the more. Peter did not question it; he knew,
he could see, that the Lord was using him, that whatever
talents and abilities he lacked were overshadowed by the
power of God which surrounded him in an almost visible
aura.

And indeed, Peter was feeding the flock. Each day two
or three or a dozen would be overwhelmed by the force
of his preaching, would repent and believe. And Peter was
helping the rest in ways he did not realize. When Peter
walked by those Christians who were timid and they saw
the granite strength of this man of God, their shoulders
squared and they found that they, too, had access to God's

power. When the tempted saw how easily Peter brushed aside all vices and temptations, they, too, found the strength to resist. And especially when Peter talked of the Scriptures, the way of righteousness came alive before them, and they became caught up with the zeal for righteousness just as he was.

Peter would not have believed it, but he was even showing the other Christians the way of love. All recognized that Peter was in love with the Christ; they saw in Peter the pinnacle of how much a man could love his Lord. Peter was unaware of it, of course. What Peter did notice was the almost mysterious way in which John loved the Lord. There was something different about that love, and especially as time went on and here and there other Christians came to show this inexplicable sort of love, Peter began to wonder afresh what Jesus had meant on that morning. He still was utterly perplexed by the conversation.

✻   ✻   ✻   ✻   ✻

The noontime is a time of relaxation and meditation. When the morning has spent itself in activities and all the day's tasks are well on the way to completion, at noontime men should sit back and review the progress of the day. In the desert patches and parched, rolling farmlands of the hot countries, all work stops during the heat of the day, and men find some quiet shade and drink the cool wine and think deep thoughts. The learned think on the greatness of mankind, the philosophers lose themselves in high metaphysics, and the common men like you and me think on the events of the morning.

As Peter and the others passed through the gates of Antioch and on through the farmlands, he was quiet, and his brows were knit in thought. The sun was at its hottest, and few were traveling. The others had begun to while away the long journey to Jerusalem with talk, some serious, some bantering, but Peter was not joining in the conversations. Peter was troubled.

For the most part the fortnight in Antioch had been wonderful. Ever since that amazing experience he had had with Cornelius at Caesarea Peter had entertained a secret, warm admiration for Paul, and for years he had been elated every time reports came in of Paul's success as Apostle to the Gentiles. And now that he had finally been able to spend some time with Paul, he admired the man all the more. The days had been warm and rich in conversation, as Peter bared his memories of the days when Jesus walked the earth, and Paul for his part revealed the depths of his understanding of the Way with ideas and concepts too great for Peter's mind. Peter had enjoyed the week immensely, lost in the pleasure of talking of the Master.

But yesterday he had been brought down to earth again. The others from Jerusalem had arrived; their presence reminded Peter of his position as a member of the chosen nation, and he was a little bit appalled by the fact that he, one of God's people, had actually been eating with gentiles. And then Paul had torn into him with such force that Peter had been completely deflated. And it had hurt.

It was not the injury to his pride that hurt Peter; what really bothered him was the realization that Paul was absolutely right. For Paul's tirade, though ostensibly directed against the unnecessary legal scruples of the Jerusalem Christians, was actually directed against something much more basic, and though the rest of the men James had sent may not have understood what lay behind the outburst, Peter did grasp it. For Paul's Christianity seemed to be based on something entirely different from that of the Jerusalem church. Paul's concept was completely divorced from righteousness as being the way to God; it was based on faith alone. Peter and Paul both were in agreement that faith was essential to Christianity; but it was Paul's understanding of the resulting position before God that was such a revelation to Peter.

Up until that time, Peter, and, so far as he knew, the great majority of the Jerusalem church, had understood Christianity to be a means of attaining righteousness before God, the same sort of righteousness that the Law commanded and Judaism purported to offer. The difference was that Jesus, by conquering death, had also conquered the power of sin in men which made it all but impossible to observe the Law. Through His power, men could now hope to achieve righteousness. Salvation was still based on observance of the Law; a life of righteousness was the only way men could please God. But Christianity made observance of the Law possible; Jesus Christ, through the power of the Holy Spirit, had now made righteousness attainable.

But Paul's idea was completely different. Paul pointed out that Jesus, in suffering on the cross, had Himself assumed all the penalties of sin, and so whoever believed in Him was absolutely free from sin in the eyes of God. Salvation was based on faith, not works of legal righteousness. For Paul, righteous living was not the ground of future salvation, but the mere index of the salvation already received.

And Peter was astounded. How could he have been so blind for all these years? He had completely overlooked the fact that the suffering of Christ was fully as important as the Resurrection. The power of Christianity was understandable under his former concept of salvation, but this idea, this revelation that Paul had shown him, also explained a whole host of other phenomena that Peter had never before stopped to wonder about. Peter was amazed that he had never thought of Christianity in that light; he was even more amazed that the others at Jerusalem, the real saints (and there were not a few) had missed it also. They had never stopped to think of Christ's sufferings as an integral part of His ministry.

But Paul had. Could the reason be the sufferings that Paul himself had undergone? Peter thought back to their conversation when he had first arrived in Antioch, when Paul had told him all the news about the spread of the Gospel, and all the trials and tribulations that had accompanied its spread. Perhaps Paul's own suffering had caused him to realize how mighty were the sufferings of Jesus, how crucial. Peter had thought Paul's attitude toward the sufferings of the Master a bit strange; now he understood.

But there was something else that was strange about Paul, something that bothered Peter. Paul loved his Lord; you could tell that at a glance. But there was something odd, something almost mysterious about his love, something Peter could not put his finger on. It was the same sort of puzzling quality Peter had noticed before in John and in other Christians here and there. It was almost as though this sort of love were deeper and larger than Peter's. And yet Peter could find no flaws in his love for Jesus. He knew that he loved his Lord with all his strength, with all his being. He had told Jesus that on that morning, and what was true then was even more true now, for Peter's capacity to love had been expanding as he grew older. Yet he wondered about the way Paul loved Jesus; he just could not understand it.

❊   ❊   ❊   ❊   ❊

If any part of the day is intolerable, it is mid-afternoon. The day's heat becomes oppressive, sweat no longer feels clean and cathartic but sticky and uncomfortable, and the little troubles that occur during the day accumulate until tempers break and raw nerves stand exposed. Mid-afternoon was particularly unenjoyable in Rome. Fish and produce in the markets joined with litter in the gutters to produce a noisome smell, the water at the fountains became tepid and unpalatable, humidity rising from the river made Rome impossible in mid-afternoon.

Peter was relaxed in spite of the chains during the long march to the place of crucifixion. His body bent with age, he was oblivious of his surroundings, of the young, sweaty Roman guards, of the jeers from the markets and windows as they went by, even of the whips that sang and snapped regularly. He was almost relieved that the time had finally come, that the long months of prison were over, that soon he would see Jesus again.

He was not joyful. He knew full well where they were taking him, and just as Jesus had predicted so long ago, he did not want to go. And yet, in a way, he was glad. Now at last the prediction could haunt him no more, now his love was actually being put to the test. He did not fear the cross. He could imagine what it would be like, but he did not fear it. He almost welcomed it, in fact. The other time Jesus had made a prediction about him, Peter had failed miserably. This time, however, it was not his courage that was being tested, but his love. And he knew that his love would not fail. Right now, as they were approaching the place, he loved Jesus more than he ever had. All through his ministry he had loved Jesus desperately, passionately. Now, in the hour of trial, he loved Him so much that it left him breathless, made the hair at the back of his neck rise. The young do not understand such love; only the old, the ones who have seen sixty and seventy years pass, are capable of such heights of love. Peter did not fear the cross; he knew that his love for Jesus would not fail.

Then all around they heard the bloodthirsty undertone of the crowd. The guards made them stop, and the victims were given an opportunity to make their last statement. When Peter's turn came, his short, simple witness to the truth was so rich with the love for Jesus which welled up out of his being that even the Roman mob was hushed. Never had anyone seen a love so deep, so remarkable as Peter's.

The spell lasted only a moment, and then the crowd came to life as the crosses were assembled and the nails prepared. The scream of the first Christian to be nailed to his cross was followed by a thundering, reverberating roar as the crowd reacted in unison like a ravenous, crazed beast. The tumult increased in intensity as another and then another cross was lifted into place, then died down in breathless anticipation as Peter's turn came. There was a murmur of awe from the crowd, for the look on Peter's face as he stretched himself on the cross was that of a conqueror. And he felt like a conqueror. He was dying for the Lord he loved; he was being tested, and his every emotion was overflowing with his love. He knew that his love for Jesus was right now the greatest he had ever felt; from this test he would emerge victorious to greet his King.

And then they drove the first nail.

Peter's whole mind reeled under the shock of pain. His left arm felt torn to shreds, his every muscle recoiled in the spasm. He gritted his teeth on his tongue to keep from crying out. He had never dreamed that the pain would be like this. With all his strength he grasped his love for Jesus, his mind repeated at breakneck speed, "I love Him, I love Him, I love Him."

And then they drove the second nail.

The pain was twice that of the first nail. It hit him like a solid wall, and as his muscles reacted the pain from his other hand rushed in afresh, a crimson, screaming tidal wave. His mind was tumbling over and over, his thoughts were racing this way and that, desperately seeking escape from the fires. His reason had been snuffed out under the second great onslaught, he clung desperately to love, not love for Jesus now or love as a meaningful emotion, but love as all he could find to grasp hold of.

And then they nailed his feet.

This time the pain was not pain but Monster. It had a thousand eyes of lightning, claws three feet long, jaws of white hot madness. Chaos reigned in Peter's mind as his body writhed from it. No sense or order there, just the dervish whirl of the insanity of pain. All was confusion, impossibility. Love was love was what? was hate! His mind shot on out over the precipice and down, down into insanity and the fires of hell. Screaming as he fell, he opened his mouth for the curses that were now unleashed.

Every man has a breaking point. That Peter's came so quickly was not so much a sign of weakness as it was a sign of his mere individuality. A man's breaking point is not determined by how brave or how stoic he is, but by what sort of individual he happens to be. Nor was the fact that his love so suddenly turned to hatred and the curses of a demon a sign that Peter's love was weak or unreal. Though a man may love with all his soul, though his emotions be indescribable, when the breaking point has come, that love will turn into its twin sister, hate, as the man is broken on the racks of torture. Not hatred of something;

just general, universal hatred. No man can love — anyone, anything — when pain has overpowered him.

Peter's face was a contorted, demonic picture of hate; his mouth opened wide, he drew in his breath to scream out the curses, and then something happened. The curses left, the chaos vanished in the cool light of reason, as the amazing thought cut through the torture: Jesus Christ had already borne his sufferings. Peter had borne as much as he could, and then he had broken, he had been ready to deny his Lord for a second and final time. But just at that moment he had felt the torture lift, almost as a physical act he had felt the Christ take the suffering from him.

Peter was astounded, dismayed. For the first time in his long life, Peter's spirit was completely, utterly broken. The realization that he would so willingly deny the Lord did not injure his pride, it destroyed it. Peter felt wretched, mean, worthless, vain. He felt lower than a worm, utterly contemptible. No longer did he think of himself as the chosen leader of the new movement; he thought of himself as the outcast, the refuse of it. "The last shall be first, and the first last." What wretch who bore the name Christian was as low as he?

And then he thought of Jesus. He had always prized the fact that he had been one of the very closest of Jesus' friends, he had always loved Jesus in the warm, close way that a man loves his friend. But now he realized what that saying meant that others had so often emphasized, indeed, which he himself had used with little or no comprehension of its significance, that Jesus is the Son of God. He saw now the unthinkable gulf that stood between himself, who had broken under the first, gentlest trials of torment, and the infinite divinity of Jesus, who had borne the very worst torture of all the evil that ever existed, borne it unconquered, without a hint of breaking.

And then the final wonder struck him, that Jesus, very God of very God, had stooped so far down that He called even Peter His friend. Jesus had loved him, had loved him in spite of the wretchedness and slime, had loved him so much that He had offered Himself, had borne the sufferings that at that very moment should have been his due portion. Peter no longer loved Jesus, not the way he had before; he felt too unworthy, too grimed and small. A new sort of love was possessing him. Now that his mind had grasped his own wretchedness, a different kind of love was his, a love of awe and respect, a love of insignificant creature for Infinite Creator. No more was his love merely emotional; it was primarily rational, it was based on the intellectual realization of what he was and who Jesus is.

A wry smile crossed his face. So this was what Jesus had been driving at on that morning long ago. Peter at long last realized that what Jesus had been looking for in him was not the love that comes from within man, for however strong that love may be, it cannot stand the test. Jesus was looking for the love that comes not from man but from God Himself, comes as the free gift of God's revelation of Himself.

Peter's body still ached impossibly. His hands and his feet were still branding irons of pain. But it no longer bothered him; though he was in the severest pain, he was no longer suffering. In some mysterious way Jesus had removed once and for all his sufferings. Instead, Peter was almost ecstatic with joy, and with the deep, fathomless love of God Himself that was welling up in him. Peter understood now why Jesus had insisted on that particular kind of love, why He had been dissatisfied with the conglomerate of emotions Peter had offered from his own paltry store.

✳   ✳   ✳   ✳   ✳

The evening is a quiet time, a time when all the hurry and bustle of the day seem to lose their importance as they are replaced by other, calmer things. The evening is the time when the tired sun bathes the countryside with shadows and hues, when mists rise from the ground and touch everything with subtle, ineffable mystery, when gossamer webbing appears on branch and leaf. The evening is the time for sleep, a time when love is near and oh, so comforting, when the mind drifts off into gentle slumber to awaken in what seems only moments to the glory of the coming day.

Peter's mind was becoming foggy as death drew near. His blood seemed gathered at his head and there was no longer keenness or sharpness in his imagination. His mind wandered dreamily as memories rose to caress him, as thoughts lazily drifted by, thoughts of comfort and peace. After the trauma of the first few minutes, the cross had actually been no burden to him; he had been bathed in the wonder of his newfound Jesus, he had been drenched in the love of One who he now realized was too great for his human conception.

And other things had been happening to him during the past three or four hours, things marvelous and overflowing. There was something rich and deep in suffering with his Lord; we who have not ourselves plumbed the depths of suffering with Him cannot imagine the meanings that lie in suffering, we would blench at the hint of them. But Peter now knew those things; with Paul, with James, with Stephen, with the hosts of martyrs gathered on the shores of eternity, Peter now had shared in the suffering of the Lamb.

It seemed to Peter as though all that he was had vanished, as though during just those first few minutes of terror God had torn down all the scaffolding that Peter had built during his life, all the facade, not only that which sin had built, but even all the things which Peter, in his clouded understanding of reality, had nurtured as parts of the Christian way: all these things had been torn down, leaving only the naked, small, childish core of the real Peter. And then the Lord had gone to work constructing a palace on the ruins, a structure of solidity and integrity that never again would be shaken, that could even pass unscathed through the impenetrable barrier of death. And Peter saw now that it had to be done that way; for all his sincerity, for all the lasting monuments of his service that would remain in the hearts of men, for all his leadership and love and faith, Peter would not have been able to survive the crisis of death as he was. But God had built something new, something permanent. Peter had often wondered during his years in the vineyard why some Christians were struck down in the prime of life, why some scarce got their teeth into their ministry when they received the call to go on; now he understood. Such men were the real saints, the ones who had allowed God to build in them just what He wanted, who would not need another ten or forty years before they could finish the course set for them.

And Peter also knew now the answer Job had sought and found, the answer he himself had often sought when he saw blameless Christians in the throes of torment. For Peter had experienced suffering now; he had found the thousand things that lie only in suffering, things unthinkable and incredibly deep. A wry thought crossed his mind as he thought of the letters he had written while in prison, especially that one in which he had talked of suffering. How inadequate, how superficial his understanding of suffering had been at that time. He could not remember having said anything that proved to be untrue, but he just had not known then the limitless glory of suffering with Jesus, he had not imagined there could be so much to it. But as he thought of it, as he tried to pen an imaginary letter now, he came to the conclusion that even now he would probably not say much more about suffering, for suffering is too intensely personal to be communicable. Regardless of how he should try to explain it, no one who had not suffered would understand, and those who had would know already.

But these thoughts were not really important; they were mere will-o'-the-wisps that flitted lazily across his mind. He saw death approaching now, and he welcomed it, for through the veil he saw the comforting, familiar face of the One he had missed so desperately all these long years. He reached out his hand to greet his Friend, and even as his thoughts were leaving the confines of mortality and entering into the splendor of Life he remembered that dawn, and at last it could trouble him no more. Now he had suffered, and finally he understood.

Appendix

Appendix

Most of the quotations of Scripture in the body of the book have been taken from the *Berkeley Version of the Bible*.

The following list contains Scriptural references pertaining to each of the stories. Immediately after the title, the reference is given from which the story was drawn. Underneath are listed references pertinent to the story but which are not to be found in the basic passage. They are preceded by a page number and a phrase to identify the location within the text of the story.

1. *The Merchant:* Genesis 18:17-33.
    Superscription: Genesis 18:32.
    P. 18 — "perhaps Lot was not righteous in all respects": compare Genesis 13:12, 13; 19:8, 30-38. But contrast II Peter 2:7, 8.
    P. 19 — "Mount Moriah": Genesis 22:1-19.
2. *The Harlot:* Joshua 2:1-22.
    Superscription: Joshua 2:9.
    P. 36 — "come to get her": Joshua 6:22, 23.
3. *The Nameless:* Ruth 1-4.
    Superscription: Ruth 4:1.
    P. 40 — "Levirate marriage": Deuteronomy 25:5-10.
    P. 41 — "Moses' curse": Deuteronomy 23:3, 4.
    P. 43 — "jubilee": Leviticus 25:8-24.
4. *The Patriot:* Jonah 1-4.
    Superscription: Jonah 4:2.
    P. 49 — "foretold the expansion": II Kings 14:25.
5. *The Forerunner:* Matthew 11:2-6; Luke 7:19-23.
    Superscription: Luke 7:29.
    P. 63 — Herod's visits: Mark 6:20.
    P. 64 — "Pharisees had sent men": John 1:19-24.
    P. 65 — "voice of God call [Jesus] son": Matthew 3:17; Mark 1:11; Luke 3:22.
    — "God had called David His son": Psalm 2:7.
    — "Egypt . . . Ephesus": Acts 18:24, 25; 19:1-4.

APPENDIX

P. 66 — "to kill Him because of . . . the Sabbath": John 5:16.
P. 67 — "passage from Isaiah": Isaiah 35:4-6.
6. *The Thief:* Luke 23:39-43.
Superscription: Luke 23:42.
P. 76 — Sheol: compare Job 3:13-19; 10:21, 22.
P. 81 — *Rex Judaeorum:* Luke 23:38; John 19:19-20.
— "a shout rose . . . and another": Luke 23:35; Mark 15:31-32.
P. 82 — "He saved others": Mark 15:31, 32.
7. *The Demon:* Matthew 28:1-8; Mark 16:1-9; Luke 24:1-12; John 20:1-16.
Superscription: Matthew 12:45.
P. 89 — "she . . . had been that way before": Matthew 27: 57-61; Mark 15:46-47.
— "spices they had mixed": Luke 23:56.
P. 90 — "the two men had wrapped His body with spices": John 19:39, 40.
8. *The Doubter:* John 20:24-29.
Superscription: John 11:16.
P. 101 — "We do not know where you are going": John 14:5.
P. 103 — "once he went fishing": John 21:2, 3.
9. *The Diplomat:* Acts 6:1 - 8:1.
Superscription: Acts 7:51.
P. 112 — "Jesus had commissioned them": Acts 1:8.
10. *The Missionary:* Acts 8:5-40.
Superscription: Acts 21:9.
P. 118 — List of deacons: Acts 6:5.
— Jesus and the Samaritan woman: John 4:22.
P. 119 — Peter and the centurion: Acts 11:4-18.
P. 123 — "his Master's greatest promise": Matthew 28:20.
11. *The Betrayer:* John 21:15-19.
Superscription: John 21:17.
P. 127 — "plunge into the lake": John 21:7.
P. 129 — "he had heard that question before": John 13:38.
— Peter's wife: Mark 1:30.
P. 131 — Pentecost: Acts 2:1-41.
P. 133 — Antioch: Galatians 2:11-16.
P. 140 — "The last shall be first . . .": Matthew 19:30.
P. 144 — "in which he had talked of suffering": I Peter 3:18; 4:1, 2; 12-19.